Desert Wells

Desert Wells

ALICE BATES

Beautiful is love, and to be free
Is beautiful, and beautiful are friends.
Love, freedom, comrades, surely make amends
For all the thorns through which we walk to death!
God let us breathe your beauty with our breath.

from 'Enslaved' by John Masefield

DARTON · LONGMAN + TODD

To you,
with love

First published in 2011 by
Darton, Longman and Todd Ltd
1 Spencer Court
140 – 142 Wandsworth High Street
London SW18 4JJ

ISBN: 978-0-232-52790-2

A catalogue record for this book is available from the British Library

Printed and bound in Great Britain by CPI Antony Rowe, Chippenham

Contents

Foreword

These stories can be read in a number of different ways.

First and foremost, they can be read just as stories. Each one has its own compelling characters and its own intriguing plot. Each draws the reader in, so that we care what happens.

Next, the reader will notice that although the stories are far from frivolous, they do lighten the heart. Many of the people involved in these stories are facing life in all its harshest reality, but they are not beyond hope. There is no sentimentality in the resolutions that start to take shape, but there is profound, believable change. These are stories about how the depth of human pain can bring out the heights of human resourcefulness.

But then, the reader may begin to wonder why each story is prefaced with a verse from the Bible. God is not mentioned in the stories, nor is hope and transformation obviously due to divine action. But re-reading the story in the light of the Bible verse is illuminating. These are stories about the profound changes that can be brought about when we really pay attention to those around us, the kind of careful, loving, expectant attention that God pays to each one of us.

The Bible knows the power of a good story, and how it can bring more insight than hours of 'teaching'. Jesus was a wonderful story-teller, often leaving his audiences puzzling over the meaning, while they shook with laughter or tears. Alice Bates' stories show again that there are all kinds of truth that we can only learn if our hearts and our imaginations are engaged.

So read them and start to pay attention to the people and things all around that can lead to freedom, growth and joy.

JANE WILLIAMS, LAMBETH PALACE, LONDON

Acknowledgements

I would like to thank the following for their help in writing this book:

John Elk III for permission to use his photograph 'Tracks across dunes, Erg Chebbi desert, Morocco' on the front cover;

Sister Seonaid Crabtree of Malling Abbey, who with Capt Jeremy Palmer and Wendy Mills provided me with the flying material for *Flying*; and Flt Lt Tim Blackwell of 129 (Tunbridge Wells) Squadron Air Training Corps, who helped with the initial research and pointed me in many helpful directions. Sister Seonaid also introduced me to the very useful exercise to be found in the notes to *The Phone Call*;

William Harper, ex-probation officer at Blantyre House, who for *Amy's Visit* kindly explained the Sycamore Tree course to me and patiently took me through the various options open to ex-offenders on release;

Sarah Leedham, A Rocha's Community Liaison Officer at Minet Country Park, who for *Buttercups* painstakingly took me through the issues involved in developing a country park from wasteland, who educated me in the flora and fauna I might find there, and whose enthusiasm was such an encouragement;

Dr Paul Worthley and Dr Alasdair Clarke from Burrswood Hospital, who for *The Bear* so kindly gave up a great deal of their time to brief me on the progressive stages of MS; in memory of Jenny Curtiss whom I had the honour to call my friend, and in warm remembrance of her husband David. I am also very grateful to those generous people whose videos on the MS website taught me so much: especially Dale Edberg, Jennifer Mason, Amy Rowell and Linda Lindsay, who gave me my title; and Cherry Bates for her memories of nursing, and especially what it feels like to be a young nurse in training;

Nicole Snashall, Professor of Mathematics at the University of Leicester, for introducing me to the golden ratio for *Living* and for kindly checking my facts; Detective Sergeant Timothy Court for kindly advising me on the police material, and for his most helpful editing suggestions;

Christina Rees for liking the story I showed her enough to intoduce me to her publisher, for which kindness I shall always be grateful;

And lastly the Revd Steve Clark, then Senior Chaplain at Burrswood Hospital, who by once asking me to write a story around a verse of Scripture started me on the journey of this book, and therefore has much to answer for!

I submitted each story on completion to a trio of dear friends for their comment and correction, and the loving support and attention to detail they were willing to lavish on me astounds me still. So I would like to thank most particularly Sister Seonaid Crabtree, Virginia Catmur and Kay Steward – only one of whom is a trained copy editor, but all of whom performed that task with more care than I had any right to expect and greatly more understanding than I could ever have hoped for. Bless you for giving up your precious time, for your wisdom and thoughtfulness, and for being the light in my darkness through many dark nights!

My endlessly patient and encouraging editor at Darton Longman and Todd, Virginia Hearn, also saw each story on completion. I'm more grateful to her than I know how to express for her friendship, kindness and steadfast support.

And finally, to all my dear family and stalwart friends who have put up with me, loved me through one missed deadline after another and supported me through thick and thin – to the many who have so faithfully prayed for me, especially my dear Sisters at Malling Abbey and my dear church family at St Matthew's, High Brooms – including Fleur Parratt, Helen Steven and Matt Taylor who knew the importance of celebrating with me when I finally finished – *thank you!* You made it possible, and I'm so very grateful for your love.

ALICE BATES, DECEMBER 2010

To begin

'And who is my neighbour?' asked an expert in the law. In reply Jesus said, 'A man was going down from Jerusalem to Jericho ...' [1], and just like that you're in a different world.

And, as so often with the stories that Jesus told, this is not a 'religious' story. It is a story about how to live. Other stories Jesus told, equally not 'religious', are about God's love for us ('There was a man who had two sons ...' [2], 'A certain man was preparing a great banquet ...' [3]).

Why tell it as a story?

Presumably because his hearers would remember the lesson better that way; but surely also because Jesus wanted to root his hearers' relationship with God right there in their ordinary, everyday lives. He told them stories about people they knew and situations they were familiar with. He brought the scripture people knew out of the synagogue and into the streets, into everybody's daily life. It was there that they would find God.

The same is true for us. What is the point of God, if he doesn't inhabit, and change, my everyday, ordinary life? If it is *not* true that Jesus Christ is both God and man and lived, died and was resurrected to eternal life for our sake, those of us who believe it are, as St Paul says, 'to be pitied more than all men [4]'.

But if it's true, then how do I respond?

I'm hampered by the fact that if God is God, by definition my understanding of him will be limited; if I did fully understand, that would indicate that my understanding was greater than his, and such a

[1] Luke 10:30
[2] Luke 15:11
[3] Luke 14:16
[4] 1 Corinthians 15:19

creature would not be God to me.

He is so far beyond me that I always, as it were, glimpse him out of the corner of my eye. He is in the spaces between things, in the connections.

But he is also so close to me that, born a human being like me, he shares my own flesh. And as such, other than in Scripture, I will find him nowhere but here: in my everyday experience, now.

So I thought it would be interesting to look at these connections: to take a verse of Scripture together with a concern we're likely to share and tell a story in the light of both, which has something to say about how we live now. What does what Jesus said two thousand years ago look like now, in a story about us? Could such a story help to 'earth' the Scripture in our daily, ordinary lives, as did the stories Jesus told?

Here are ten stories that attempt to do this: through which we might re-examine how we honour our relationships and live our lives. Perhaps they may open windows into new ways of looking at things, rather than give answers; revive our imaginations and give us back a sense of wonder and hope, both for the creation around us and for ourselves.

These stories seek to throw some light on what stops us loving others and how we might grow in love, so that, as we chew over the characters and the situations they find themselves in, as we apply to our own lives their troubles and their solutions, we may begin to see ourselves and those around us in a new light: precious, holy and full of possibility.

I trust that there will be resonances in the stories which are simply personal to you, that you will enjoy following through.

I also hope this may be a refreshing approach for study in church house groups, and there are some notes at the back to help with this. I've kept them general: they are meant only to be a starting-point, so that group leaders can develop the ideas as they wish.

There is a logical sequence to the themes which I hope will become clear if you read this book from the beginning (though of course you can dip in and out if you prefer to read it that way!). Scripture, theme and story go together. I hope you will enjoy exploring the connections that they make for you.

1. The Real Thing

SLOW DOWN

'The wise heart will know the proper
time and procedure.'
Ecclesiastes 8:5b

The two tramps lay at a short distance from each other outside Charing Cross station. They weren't a pretty sight. One of them, curled up like a cat on the pavement at the foot of the metal stairway among the discarded chip bags and greasy bits of carton and used condoms, was facing the noxious stone wall which had stood in for a toilet on several occasions the previous night. He was a large man, though thin; all that was visible of his head was the clump of matted and dirty grey hair poking above the collar of his threadbare jacket. It was impossible to tell what colour the jacket had once been (stretched tight across his bony shoulders though it was, an expanse which pitifully exposed frayed ends, lost stitching and holes); perhaps the material had once been denim. His trousers, unpleasantly caked and stained, ended raggedly and too soon above knotty, discoloured ankles and shoes which, having more than discharged their useful purpose several years previously, had entered into an uneasy reincarnation with the aid of old newspaper and scrags of string.

The other tramp was sitting against the railings on the other side of the stairway with his knees up, smoking a cigarette. He had a narrow face, dusty brown hair and small eyes of no particular colour. He was wearing a grey pin-striped suit that looked as if someone had thrown it out after a prolonged period of wearing it to do the gardening; an old grey vest and, perhaps in memory of better days, the remnant of a red neckerchief. On his feet he had stained trainers that had once been white.

It was just short of eight o'clock on a clear April morning. The tramps were the only stationary elements in the sea of commuters that pressed up and down the metal stairway linking Charing Cross British Rail and the lane down to Embankment tube station, dividing and rejoining around them like tidal water round boulders, as driven and as unaware; people's feet finding the only possible space before, as they moved on, someone else stepped where they had been.

Many negotiated their way with a briefcase in one hand and a mobile phone in the other. Here and there some, having engineered their way to the edges and twisted themselves into a corner, were holding an old envelope or a notebook against a wall while writing instructions, keeping the phone in place with their shoulder; some were reading a compactly-folded newspaper as they went; many wore earphones.

The tramp with his knees up drew deeply on his cigarette, exhaled, and addressed the other one. 'What I don't understand is why you have to be quite so disgusting.'

'Because,' replied the other without moving, 'there is one today who needs to see past the filth to the person underneath. Compassion can only begin if a person sees the other person.'

'But of course they see the other person. How can they not? There you are, and in the state you are especially, how can they miss you?'

'Has anyone seen *you*, lately?'

The tramp with the cigarette set it down carefully, disengaged his back from the railings and stood up. He stepped forward into the press of people, which instantly and automatically parted around him and continued on its way without pausing, even momentarily.

'Apparently not.' The second tramp sat down again and picked up his cigarette. 'But I don't understand. What has happened to them?'

'They are preoccupied.'

'You know that is not the answer.'

'Very well. They're not aware. They choose a little life because it is a life they can control, and this society is built on apparent achievement and success as defined by the people themselves. Therefore their vision is small. They compete one against the other, and the most important thing is to be seen as sharper, stronger and better than the next person. To be seen as able to control outcomes is therefore all-important; and the surrender of self to another which true life requires is, to them, absurd. This culture suffers from an impoverishment of the imagination.'

'But that's not true of all of them.'

'No, but it's true of large numbers of the ones around us at this moment. Which is why we're here, not somewhere else.'

'And the others? The ones of whom this isn't true?'

'They're doing elsewhere the same job we're doing here.'

'Which is what, precisely?'

'Being present.'

Vince hurried along the platform, pulling Sophie by the hand behind him. He wasn't late – if anything he was early today, which was surprising under the circumstances. His partner Jackie was away on business and the childminder had phoned in sick, and, it being the Easter holidays, he'd had to bring Sophie in with him. It was just one of those things.

So he wasn't rushing because he was late. He rushed habitually; partly because of a mental attitude of wanting to 'get on', and partly because he hated the process of the journey: the train, the people, the fuss – the cold or the heat or the rain, whichever it was that day. He just wanted to get to the office as fast as possible.

This had much to do with the fact that he worked on the plum account of a top London advertising agency. He knew he was a lucky man. He'd longed for it and planned for it and, finally, his efforts had been recognised and six weeks ago he'd landed it: he was now part of the gifted team managing one of the biggest brands in the world. He still couldn't believe it. At any given time of day or night he simply wanted to be there, *doing* it. It consumed him: the buzz, the excitement, the sheer creative energy – the heady knowledge that he was now world-class.

And if things didn't happen to be going quite so well, he wanted to be there all the more.

Sophie, breathless from being dragged along too fast and from the effort involved in avoiding briefcases, bulky bags and passengers who suddenly stopped for no apparent reason, was excited. She was silent because she was trying to take in everything at once with no pause-time: ads and billboards and interesting-looking people and station-roof ironwork and platform layout and the fact that she was quite sure she'd just seen a little grey mouse scuttle across the tracks between the buffers and the front of the stationary train they'd just stepped off.

Sophie had never been to London before. Sophie was seven.

'Here.' Vince gave Sophie her ticket. 'You put it in that machine there. No – look – like this.' Vince slipped his ticket into the barrier's slot and took it out at the other end as the barrier opened and he walked through. 'Now you.'

Sophie repeated the process, startled and enchanted by the silky movement of the mechanism as it took her ticket: it was like when her dog Tinker lifted titbits from her fingers when no-one was looking. And she enjoyed how the action of taking her ticket again opened the two sides of the barrier to let her through. She wondered how exactly it did it. And then she was out onto the station concourse and there was such a tumble of interesting things – a Smiths with sweets and crisps and a place that sold socks and lots of food places with lovely smells – pizza and pastries and coffee – and a kind of hot, dry, dusty, oily kind of general smell underneath – and a machine you could get a newspaper out of and a man with a ponytail and a tattoo of a blue fish on his arm with a cleaning-up trolley and –

'For heaven's sake, come *on*, Sophie!' Vince grabbed her hand and pulled her across to the far side, where there was a stairway that led down to the street.

Sophie lost Vince in the crush of people pressing forwards to go down the stairway. She found she was simply lifted off her feet and carried down – an unsettling but interesting experience she had not had before. She was captivated by the narrow little street she was being carried down to: it was like a street at the bottom of a well, she thought, all tall sides and peeling paint; and the skinny houses opposite looked squeezed up tight as if they hadn't had enough room to grow. They had crooked little ground-floor shops elbowing each other onto the street, with umbrellas and scarves and teddy bears tied to the door frames, cramped front windows piled up with little statues and cushions and necklaces and – oh, everything! She longed to explore them.

When her feet touched the ground again she was all but across the street. She looked around for Vince but couldn't see him anywhere – though it was difficult in the pressing crowd, her eyes being on a level with everyone else's chest. So she looked ahead and straight in front of her she saw a ship.

The ship was a sailing ship and it was racing. She could see how fast it was going by the way the waves were smacking against the hull and being flung back in gusts of spray, feathery white against the shiny black. She had never seen so many sails on a ship: there were rows and rows of them. She counted three main masts and each one had five – and six – and five – huge, swelling sails; but also each mast had spars out to the side that carried smaller, squarer sails, and there were four triangular ones attached in front of the first mast, and at least one other large square one attached behind the rearmost mast – she couldn't quite see. They were all puffed out in a strong wind, with the sun blazing on their snowy whiteness and throwing sharp dark shadows behind them. The underneath of the sails, where you could see it, was a soft gold colour.

Sophie was transfixed. Had she been able to articulate it, it was the combination of power and simplicity that held her rooted to the spot: the ranks of fat, taut sails supported by so slender a hull so perfectly designed to slice through water. The sweep from the low stern to the tip of the high bowsprit which extended the line of the deck was a soaring single curve which took her breath away. The ship was flying, real, alive.

She realised she was looking at a poster of a painting, stuck up in a shop window. Under the poster there was a wooden model ship on a stand. It was about fifteen inches tall and carefully made, with intricate rigging and rolled-up sails and neat little lifeboats. It had a brass plaque on the front that said 'CUTTY SARK 1869.'

'How beautiful,' Sophie breathed, looking at the poster. 'How lovely.'

When Vince lost Sophie's hand he was alarmed but not unduly worried. Everyone was going the same way and she was a sensible child, she wouldn't wander off. His mind went at once to the problem that now nagged at him perpetually, like toothache.

The truth was, he knew he was struggling.

Having won such an accolade as this hotly-contested job he was desperate to prove he deserved his place and to make a contribution, but the weeks were slipping by and it was as if the spirit inside him had withered and died. Account executives had to be hard-working, energetic, well-organised and disciplined – all qualities he knew he possessed – but on the top accounts they had to have something else too: flair, imagination, the quicksilver twist in a creative idea that took it from good to brilliant; that's what you were paid for, and you wouldn't stay on a top account for long in such a competitive industry if you couldn't produce it. And, so far, he hadn't.

He'd thought he was creative, but now he profoundly doubted it. It was as if he'd been able to come up with offbeat and imaginative concepts just as long as he didn't have to; but that kind of individual creative voice isn't as common as you might think or wish, and it had been spotted. Now it had been given free rein; now he depended on it; and it had vanished.

Perhaps it was that he'd shone simply because everyone around him had been more dull – like an angel-fish in a tank of sprats – but someone had scooped him out and released him instead into the sunny waters of a coral reef where he had always felt, instinctively, that he belonged; only he must have been mistaken. It was the other fish now who were the beautiful ones, and he had no business there.

Very soon, he knew, it would be noticed. Perhaps it already had been.

Oh, he had a full diary all right – there were meetings, conferences, various 'pitches' to prepare – he was busy. Tomorrow he had his first client campaign briefing and he'd spent the last few days preparing for it, working his way through meetings with his account manager, the creative team and the research staff. He'd planned to spend today putting the finishing touches to his presentation, as well as looking at some ideas for a new project just to keep his mind fresh.

But it was no good; what he had for tomorrow was perfectly acceptable, but he knew deep down that it had no spark. And he was terrified.

He realised with a start that he was standing in the middle of the narrow street outside Charing Cross station with other commuters pressing past on every side, but he'd forgotten Sophie altogether. He looked around for her – blimey, they needed to clear up the streets, there were two quite disgusting blokes over by the stairs up to the station, and he hoped Sophie hadn't seen them – and after a few moments of mounting anxiety, spotted her staring into a shop window some twenty feet away. Relieved, he made his way over to her.

'Finally, Sophie! I was worried, I couldn't see you. Come on!'

'Dad, look! There's this ship – '

'Not now, Sophie, ok? Another time. Got to get to work,' said Vince, taking her hand and pulling.

'No, Dad! *Please!*'

Something in her voice stopped him. He recognised it: it was that special something, that genuine thrill that he couldn't find in himself. It stopped him dead.

'Look,' said Sophie.

Vince looked in the shop window and saw a pretty little model ship. He read the name on the brass plaque and smiled. He'd made a model of the *Cutty Sark* when he was little older than Sophie was now.

'That's nice, Sophie,' he said, remembering the smell of the glue, the sheer joy of the little pots of paint and borrowing his dad's small screwdriver to open them with; the business of finding newspaper for covering the dinner table, and sandpaper for smoothing . 'Do you like models? We could – '

'No, no,' said Sophie. 'Not the *model*, Dad! The real thing, look!'

Vine raised his eyes. The lovely ship cut through the water before him, living, soaring, her full sails stretching, leaning slightly towards him in the speed of her going as the wind punched the canvas. He smelled the clean briny rush of her and heard the thud of the waves against her hull.

And as he watched her power through the water he thought how silly it was to make a model that would sit on a stand, to be looked at as if she were meant to be stiff and still rather than a living thing, built to respond to the pressure of the sea, to plunge round and change tack, to drive ahead at speed, to swing on the lilting swell of a little harbour when the storm was spent. You could reproduce the physical shapes of the hull and the deck and the spars and you could carefully glue a brass plaque onto it; but you couldn't reproduce the soaring life of her, the thrill of the race, the smack of the wind, the taste of salt on your lips.

A ship is nothing out of the water, her sails furled, her hull stilled.

Vince looked at intention so triumphantly realised and his heart leaped. He thought about the Victorian ship owner who'd commissioned the ship that would be first home with the new season's crop of tea from China – just such a commercial imperative as drove his own work – and the designer who'd sat down to deliver it. Stop, stop. What is wanted here? A hull designed for speed, but also strong enough to withstand the southern oceans; with as large a cargo capacity as possible; able to support as large a sail area as possible. Designed to bring home successfully the most, the fastest.

It struck Vince like a blow that it is the very unyielding knottiness of your raw material or required parameters that brings forth something new and beautiful. You don't create in a vacuum; what are you working *with?* The song written for *that* singer and no other; the play required to showcase the gifts of *that* comic actor; you take things that *are*, and coax them into some new form that's not only thrilling in itself, but is faithful to the character of what you started with.

Not only that, but if I'm the one doing the creating, thought Vince, my own gifts and insights are central too. So the question for me is not, oh God oh God, what can I *do*, but what particular actual thing or set of circumstances, out of all the ones around me, is the one upon which I can build some new reflection or combination that is true, because it resonates with me? What is true for *me?*

It's being faithful to what you start with *and* being faithful to what you are yourself, thought Vince, that will produce the real thing. He had never thought of it that way before.

He realised he'd been standing still for some minutes. He couldn't remember when that had last happened, and he drew a long breath. He squinted up at the sky, which was that clear pale blue you get after rain; he caught the smell of fresh croissant bought by someone who'd just pressed past him, and he followed her with his eyes – a West Indian woman wearing a bright red skirt and yellow sweater, with a green scarf tied around her waist; she stepped between people with practised grace and he admired her slim neck and the way she held her head.

When had he last really looked at anyone? Startled, he turned to other people around him and was struck by the vast variety of them: how many countries were represented in this street, he wondered? They were no longer simply a mass to be negotiated: each one had a name, a history, was on a particular journey to somewhere. Who were they? Suddenly he wanted to stop everyone and ask them where they were going, what they were doing. What they cared about.

He looked down at the top of a small fair head he knew well but hadn't really seen for a long time. Pale blond hair in a ponytail. Shiny, with soft feathery bits escaping at the edges, like the down on ducklings. He started to laugh.

Sophie looked up. 'What, Dad? What's funny?'

'You are.' Vince rubbed her head. 'Not funny ha-ha, funny *brilliant.* Sophie, you've made me look at the sky and smell a croissant and think about a beautiful ship which you said was the real thing, and I can't believe you've done all that in about ten minutes, when I haven't done any of it for months. Years. *I* don't know! I feel about twelve years old and everything's *fun*. You're the business, Sophie!

Fancy a hot chocolate? There's a nice little caf just round the corner.'

'Yes please, Dad. And can I have the poster of the ship? I have my pocket money.'

'You certainly may, but I'll get it for you myself, you keep your pocket money for something else.' He grinned at her. 'Come on, Squirrel.'

A few minutes later they came back out of the shop, Sophie happily bearing a paper tube with a rubber-band round it. She lagged slightly behind as they crossed the road and looked up to find she was bang in front of the filthiest person she'd ever seen. He was sitting cross-legged right there on the dirty pavement, and he smelled. She wrinkled her nose and recoiled slightly, and then looked at him again.

He was wearing a yucky old jacket and the most disgusting trousers, and he was all thin and scraggy. Suddenly she felt a stab of grief that anybody should end up like that, so terrible and smelly. All the adults she knew were clean and tidy and lived smooth sorts of lives. What had happened to this man to make him like that? She wondered if he was hungry, and looked into his face.

Her eyes grew wider and wider, and for the second time that day she was rooted to the spot. She was looking into deep blue eyes that weren't old at all – or at least, age didn't seem to come into it – and they were merry and solemn all at once. But what surprised her most of all was that somehow they seemed to claim kinship with her, as if the wretched old man were somebody she knew. No – as if he and she were old friends. And oddly, she knew that they were. She looked at him and she *recognised* him.

He winked at her and, as if suddenly released, she sprang from him up the pavement to where Vince was just turning to find her. 'Dad!' she called to him, 'Dad! Dad! I just saw – '

The tramp stared after her fondly. 'Now there goes a *nice* human being!', he remarked to the other. 'There's my compassionate girl. That one has a gift for being present to others, for being real, for true friendship. What she did today for her father, she will spend her life doing, for many. She looks properly. She looked at the disgusting old tramp and she saw *me*.'

'What, actually saw you?'

'Oh yes. She will remember always the cool April morning of her first trip to London, when she looked up and saw an angel.'

2. *Flying*

LISTEN

'My sheep listen to my voice; I know them,
and they follow me.'
John 10:27

Circuit Breakers – in
Master Switch – on
Fuel Selector – port tank on
Fuel Contents – check
Flaps – up
Radio – off
Mixture – rich
Carb Heat – cold
Engine – prime
Magnetos – both on

Not for the first time, Frank Boulter wondered whether he should ever have taken this job. But fifty-six had seemed early to retire, and what would he have done all day? So when the small electronics firm where he'd been a manager had amalgamated with a larger one, making him redundant, he'd looked for something else; perhaps something a little different. And he'd seen the advertisement: director of a care home for learning-disabled adults, six houses of ten residents each in an attractive woodland setting, accommodation provided.

The accommodation had been the clincher. To be honest, he'd been lonely. He and his wife had married early and they'd never had children, so when she'd died from cancer a couple of years previously he hadn't quite known what to do with himself. A job that involved relationship, people, a home; it sounded just right.

He'd been there six months now and on the whole it had delivered, though it was challenging in unexpected ways. The residents were often disruptive, but he'd expected that; to be honest the staff was worse. No, that wasn't fair. Let's face it, it was Sandy, really.

Sandy: crisp, competent, controlling. Sandy, whose pathways through the house which she managed were as unalterable as the sun's trajectory through the heavens (and in her opinion, doubtless, no less beneficial). Sandy's methods were never to be questioned.

Sandy was always right. And if Frank ever suggested anything new or different, Sandy's invariable reply was 'We don't do it like that here.'

Frank knew Sandy was very experienced and that, while he was good at general management, he had much to learn about learning disability. He knew he would get on much faster with Sandy as his friend, so he worked at it. It wasn't getting any easier, though. Sandy was one of those women who despised men; doubly so when it was a man in authority over her but without what she considered the experience necessary. The words 'I can't stand that woman' had surfaced early on in Frank's usually placid mind, and remained a sentiment which he acknowledged, then consciously set aside, daily. So it was unfortunate that there should be an incident which involved a member of Sandy's house.

It had been a nice day and there'd been a good quota of volunteers, so Sandy had sent out Oak's ten residents and four helpers to Eastbourne in the minibus for a fish and chips lunch. Their usual restaurant was busy and they'd had to wait an hour for their food, by which time even the calmest residents were getting noisy. A run on the beach afterwards to let off steam had attracted unwelcome comments from people who should have known better, and some residents had taken the opportunity to paddle in the sea, while others had fallen in as they tried to pull the first ones away, so several people were soaked through on the minibus home.

And then, Joe had seen the aeroplane.

'Clear prop!'
Starter – engage
Engine – idle at 1200rpm
Oil Pressure – rising
Oil Temp – rising
Radio – on

Frank opened Joe's file again, though he knew what was in it. It was the usual sorry tale – teenaged mum who hadn't wanted him, no father, children's home till two years ago when he'd left at sixteen to come here. And autistic.

But the notes didn't seem to add up. He was high-functioning – clever, even – but most days he just yelled. It drove the care team wild because they knew Joe chose to yell; it wasn't that he couldn't help it. He was good at maths and chess. He spoke when he wanted to and understood what was said to him. If he wanted to, he could do anything that he was asked to do; but mostly he didn't want, which further annoyed the care team.

Frank was curious. What was going on in Joe?

He had already had an unsatisfactory conversation with Sandy on the subject some weeks previously, which boiled down to his view that Joe's yelling might have a root cause which was discoverable and treatable – were they, in fact, doing all they could for him? – versus Sandy's view that that was just how he was, yelling helped him let off steam and anyway, the fact that you could calm him down with things he liked – same as the other residents – showed that he was no different and that they were taking all the right steps. What more could you expect? He was autistic, right?

'Tower, Golf Bravo Foxtrot Sierra Romeo, radio check, over.'
'Golf Bravo Foxtrot Sierra Romeo, loud and clear, strength five. How me? Over.'
'Tower, Golf Bravo Foxtrot Sierra Romeo, loud and clear, strength five. Out.'

Aeroplanes were the things Joe liked. Aeroplanes in old films like *The Dambusters* or *The First of the Few,* aeroplanes on RAF recruitment posters around the walls of his room, aeroplane models which occasionally he had the patience and concentration to work on (sometimes indeed with a concentration that was so profound it all but frightened the staff).

Frank didn't know enough about autism to press his point, but in this aspect of the case he suspected Sandy didn't, either. She wasn't an imaginative woman. She just wanted an efficient, smoothly-running house.

And he had to admit, she was right. Frank groaned. What most residents needed more than anything else was stability and order, and she provided those in bucketfuls. He might not like her but her house ran like clockwork and he had a lot to learn.

Today, however, might give Frank his opportunity. He mentally squared his shoulders and called in Ben, because Ben was Joe's 'key worker' and had been on the minibus at the time, and Sandy, because she would have come anyway if he hadn't asked her first.

'So what happened, Ben?'

Ben, a kind and careful lad, was anxious and upset.

'It was weird. I don't know! One minute everyone's just having a bit of a sing-song, and then we draw up to some lights and Joe does one of his yells, yanks his seatbelt off and rushes to the door, trying to pull it open. Luckily he couldn't, but we couldn't get him to settle and we had to literally hold him down all the way home. He just went mental.'

Sandy interrupted. 'Well, it was obvious, wasn't it? Saw a bloody aeroplane, what are we supposed to do! There were road works so they had to take a detour past some airfield, and Ben says there was a plane parked right there by the hedge, he couldn't miss it.'

Frank said, 'Has he ever seen a real aeroplane before?'

'Don't know. Don't suppose he has.' She shrugged.

'What's he doing now?'

'Yelling, mostly.' Ben looked awkward. 'Actually, having a real go, this time.'

'Not to worry.' Frank smiled at Ben. 'Tell me about Joe and aeroplanes, Ben.'

'Well, he likes the ones the Red Arrows fly. And Concorde, he can tell you all about that. And Spitfire engines. And all different cloud types, knows all the names, he's dead brilliant.'

'You know what, Sandy?' Frank stood up. 'Let's all three of us go and have a little chat with Joe.'

Park Brake – on
Visual Check behind
Engine T's and P's – all green
Throttle – open to 1800rpm
Engine T's and P's – still green
Suction – check
Magnetos – check
Ammeter – check
Throttle – close, check rpm
Throttle – open to 1200rpm

'So let me get this straight.' Sandy and Frank were sitting in the empty dining room the following morning. A good enough, impersonal place – neither his office nor her sitting room – in which to struggle to some kind of mutual understanding.

'You're saying you want to give Joe flying lessons, because yesterday he told you all he's ever wanted to do is fly a plane.' Sandy was as incredulous as if Frank had proposed sending Joe to the moon because he'd said he liked cheese.

'I want to look into the possibility of it, yes.'

'But he's autistic!' Sandy almost shouted. 'You can't just take a resident right out of what he knows and put him into something totally unfamiliar, which in this case is plain dangerous, even to you or me, never mind him! It's impossible!' She drew breath. 'Listen, it's not like ordinary life here. He doesn't do what *we* say, and he knows us. How's he going to learn? He'll kill someone. You don't know anything about autism!'

'You're right, Sandy, I don't.' Frank let that sink in. 'But you do. And anything we do for Joe, we do with you.' Frank deliberately held her gaze for a moment, then just as deliberately looked away, giving Sandy space to process what he'd said. When he raised his eyes to hers again she was watching him, waiting; but her shoulders were down and her body had relaxed.

Frank said calmly, 'Will you hear me out?'

Sandy nodded, surprising herself. She was even more surprised when, half an hour later, she found she had agreed to Joe's seeing a specialist to identify likely behavioural responses, and to Frank's approaching the local flying club regarding the possibility of lessons, should the specialist's findings prove favourable.

'Everybody deserves a chance,' Frank had said. 'And he doesn't have a mum or a dad to push for him. What if he could do it, and spent the rest of his life shut up in his room because nobody ever let him try?'

'Tower, Golf Bravo Foxtrot Sierra Romeo request taxy.'

'Sierra Romeo, taxy to holding point runway one eight. QNH one zero one five, QFE one zero one one.'

'Tower, Sierra Romeo taxying to holding point runway one eight. QNH one zero one five, QFE one zero one one.'

Flight Lieutenant Caudwell felt sad as he dialled the number of Frank's direct line. It was a real shame. He'd had lots of reservations at first and had taken things slowly, but as the weeks had gone by he'd begun to think it might actually work; in many ways the lad was an absolute natural. But now – well, unless something very radical happened, he was pulling the plug on it.

Frank listened to him, appalled. 'So what's he doing, exactly?'

'It's more what he's *not* doing. He won't take instruction. He considers something I've asked him to do is stupid, and he refuses to do it. Every check a pilot is asked to make is there for a reason, and you must understand that unless Joe does what he's taught, in every respect, I can't continue.'

'Of course – I see – '

Throttle – open to 1800rpm
Park Brake – release

Frank went first to break the news to Sandy, to get it over with. In fact he hadn't had that much to do with her in recent weeks; there had been problems in other houses which had taken up his time and which had, in passing, taught him to appreciate Sandy's efficiency. But the response he got was not what he'd expected.

'You see,' said Sandy sadly, 'it's been so good, and not just for Joe, either.' She hesitated and then said awkwardly, 'I didn't believe you. I'm sorry! But you were right. Joe's been – well, different in lots of ways. Lots quieter, more amenable, so much more relaxed. The whole house has calmed down. Everyone's happier.'

'Do you mean he's stopped yelling?'

'Yes, just about! I'd never have believed it. And I hadn't realised how much his doing that put all the others on edge.' She looked at him miserably. 'Do you think there's no chance of his carrying on, with the flying, I mean?'

'I don't know.' Astonished at this turn of events, Frank just stood for a moment, taking it in. Then he smiled at Sandy, acknowledging the new ground on which they stood together. 'Well! Let's go and talk to Joe.'

'Tower, Sierra Romeo holding at runway one eight.'

'Sierra Romeo, hold position.'

'It's the downwind checks,' said Joe sullenly. 'It's stupid, I won't do it.'

'What's stupid, Joe?'

'You have to check the undercarriage is down. In my Cessna the undercarriage is fixed, it's down already. If I am in an aeroplane with a retractable undercarriage, I will know, and then I will check that it is down before landing. But not in my Cessna, it's stupid.'

'But Joe, Flight Lieutenant Caudwell said everybody does that check, as preparation for when they might be flying a plane where it's necessary. Imagine if you made a mistake – '

'I wouldn't. I would know my aeroplane! I will do that check when I need to, I will always know what aeroplane I am in!'

Trim – set
Throttle friction – set
Mixture – rich
Fuel – on, check gauge
Flaps – set for take-off
Altimeter – set
Direction Indicator – synchronise
Harness and Hatches – secure
Controls – full and free

As Sandy sat in unaccustomed silence, Frank searched his memory for anything in Joe's file, which he had consulted earlier that morning, which might help him.

'Joe – do you remember, when you were eight, and you helped to housetrain a puppy?'

Joe's face cleared and his dark eyes lit with laughter. 'Dixie! She was a *good* dog!'

Frank and Sandy began to laugh with him, they couldn't help it, the transformation was so sudden and complete.

'What was good about Dixie, Joe?'

'When she was allowed into the house the first time, she raced round and round barking and chasing, she knocked us all over and licked us so much, she was funny!'

'Did she want to come into the house, Joe?'

'Oh yes!'

'Why didn't she come in straight away then?'

'She had to stay outside until she learned the places for wees and poos.'

'So how did you teach her what to do?'

'Picked her up and put her in the right place, lots of times – over and over.'

'So she didn't learn straight away?'

'Oh no, you had to do it over and over.'

'But in the end, she learned?'

'Yes. But we had to wait till we were sure she was *really* a good dog, before she could come in.'

'Now Joe, listen.' Frank tried to find the best words. 'Dixie didn't understand at first what she had to do, did she?'

'No.'

'But in the end she was glad she did it, wasn't she?'

'Oh yes!'

'Joe, it's the same with flying your Cessna.' Joe's bright face darkened and he turned away. 'No, please listen to me, Joe.'

Joe made a small, indeterminate gesture with his hand, which Frank took as encouragement to go on. He said gently, 'Everybody who flies a plane has to do the same thing, over and over, whatever they think of it. Otherwise they don't let you fly. Dixie had to do the same thing, over and over, whatever she thought of it. Otherwise you didn't let her in the house.'

Joe looked at him.

'When Flight Lieutenant Caudwell tells you to do something, and even after you understand it, you think it's stupid, think to yourself 'Dixie!', and do it anyway. Then he will let you fly.'

'And if I don't, he will not let me fly?'

'No. And he will be right. He has to be sure that you will do what he says, and do it right, over and over, even when he is not there to see. You had to wait till you were sure that Dixie would *always* do what you had taught her, before you let her into the house.'

There was a long pause. Joe looked at the floor, cracking his knuckles. Frank and Sandy held their breath.

'So, I will think in my head the undercarriage is a Dixie and I will say 'undercarriage down' in my downwind checks?'

'Exactly, Joe, yes. And every other time there is a Dixie.'

Joe thought about it. Frank and Sandy waited.

Then Joe smiled suddenly. 'Okay,' he said. 'Dixie was a good dog. And I am good, too.'

'Sierra Romeo, take off at your discretion runway one eight, surface wind

one eight five degrees, five knots. QNH one zero one five, QFE one zero one one. Left-hand circuit.'
'Tower, Sierra Romeo runway one eight, left hand.'

Joe checked that his approach was clear, took his feet off the brakes and steered onto the runway, lining up straight and keeping the control column steady. He took a deep breath and pushed the throttle fully open.

'Tower, Sierra Romeo rolling.'
'Sierra Romeo, Roger, report downwind.'

As the engine roared and he gathered speed, Joe held the column steady to keep the nose down, looking straight ahead the whole time but keeping an eye on his temperatures and pressures. His mind was wholly relaxed; he was alert, expectant, his hands and feet as much components of the machinery they directed as the controls themselves. He and the aeroplane were one.

He watched his speed climb and then gently eased the column back, keeping up a steady pressure as the nose came up, the horizon dropped, and he felt the wind take the aeroplane as it kicked off the ground.

And as Joe soared into the air on his first solo flight, out of sheer joy and because, now, there was nobody to hear, Joe yelled.

3. The Golden Bird

IMAGINE

'Now to him who is able to do immeasurably more than all we ask or imagine, according to his power that is at work within us, to him be glory in the church and in Christ Jesus throughout all generations, for ever and ever! Amen.'
Ephesians 3:20-21

Caroline was sitting on the doorstep of her basement bedsit one cold, rainy afternoon in October, having a cigarette and crying. It was four months to the day after her seventeenth birthday and shortly, she suspected, before her boyfriend Dave left for good. The baby, who was three months old, was asleep on the double mattress they all shared and which took up most of the floor space of the mildewed room behind her. Their clothes and other possessions were in carrier bags ranged along two of the walls. Apart from the mattress there was an old sink with a draining-board, a rusting Baby Belling cooker, a wall-mounted cupboard, a small black and white television that Dave's parents had given them, and a washing-line across one corner. Round the back outside there was a poor excuse for a shower which worked intermittently and a toilet which, fortunately, did flush. They shared these with the bedsit next door.

The two bedsits had previously formed the basement of a Victorian terraced house behind North Acton tube station, now split into flats and providing council accommodation. Next door was a Nigerian couple with their two children. They were there while the authorities decided whether they could stay in England or whether they'd have to go back to Nigeria. Caroline knew them by sight and had exchanged a few words occasionally with the mother and the little girl, whose name was Adeola; she didn't often see them because she was so taken up with her own concerns, but she felt sorry that four people should have to live in a room only a little larger than her own.

The doorstep she was sitting on was the original basement doorway onto the street. A couple of feet behind her was a partition wall with two cheap, battered doors, one for each bedsit. Caroline's door was open; she knew she shouldn't smoke around the baby so she did it outside, leaving the door open to air the room and to make sure she could hear the baby if she woke. It meant the room was mostly cold, though.

She also knew that while the baby was asleep she should be doing some washing, be thinking about making the tea and maybe tidy up a bit, but she was too tired for any of it.

Caroline had left home a year previously. Her father would come off shift at the factory where he worked and go down the pub with the lads, and her mother had a job at a local hairdresser's which was the centre of her social life; both were happy enough and expected Caroline to get on with it pretty much on her own. She went to a failing school where discipline was poor and where nobody really cared if you went or not, or whether you did your work. Nevertheless, Caroline was bright, and took a handful of 'O' levels. Then she left school and got a job in a café.

However, much to her parents' surprise and to her own, she did well in her exams, especially in maths and science.

Later in the day on which she'd received her results notification, Caroline had gone into the kitchen where her mum was reading a magazine.

'Mum, I want to try for uni.' Caroline had plunged in, the letter received that morning in her hand. Her mum had looked up.

'You what, Cass? What you mean, uni?'

'Uni, Mum, you know – university.'

Her mum had laughed. 'You're joking!'

'No, Mum. Really.'

'What for? You got a nice little job at the café, and if you don't want that, there's others. Thought you'd left school to start work, girl, earn a living! University's for toffs. Waste of time. Anyhow, we don't have the money, you know that.'

'I'd get a grant, Mum, they help you – '

'And what about all the rest of it, living expenses and that? How will you keep yourself? Whichever way you cut it, it costs. Not a chance! Put it out of your head.'

And her dad had said the same. So, after several blistering rows, she'd left.

She'd stayed for a bit with one of the girls who worked with her at the café, but to be honest she'd had no idea how to go about accessing the further education she knew she would need, and the arguments had taken their toll. She'd felt shaky and tearful a lot of the time, and had started to smoke like the other girls did. Perhaps working in a café was all she should go for, after all. It wasn't so bad!

And then she'd met Dave, who was twenty and about to start an apprenticeship with British Telecom. It wasn't exactly university, but at least he was doing something with a future to it.

'Course you can go to uni, Cass, you can get grants and that like you said, you can work in the caf or whatever for your living money. What you want to do there, anyway?'

'I'm not sure.' Caroline had felt embarrassed. 'I thought – a science, chemistry or biology, maybe. But – '

'But what?'

'Well, I know it sounds stupid, but what I think I really want to do is study medicine.'

'Wow!' Dave had looked at her with respect. 'But that's *long*, and you need amazing grades.' He'd looked at her curiously. 'You got them?'

Caroline had blushed. 'No. At least, I don't have enough 'O's in the first place, and I need to up some of the grades of the ones I do have. But I need 'A' levels too. How'm I going to do all that? That's before I even start!'

And Dave had said 'Dunno, but there'll be a way. Want to go out with me?'

So she had.

Dave was then living at home with his parents and little sisters. He hadn't known what to do after school and had had several false starts, so his parents had liked Caroline's aspirations – at first – and had got her a pile of information from the local library about courses she could take. Caroline had read through it all carefully and her spirits had risen.

There were places she could go to for advice – the local FE college, the job centre – and she could study part-time as well as work. It was too late for the proper start of this academic year, but she might be able to start studying as early as January.

But long before January, she'd started being sick every day.

The GP had thought she had an inflammation of the stomach and referred her to the gastroenterology department at the hospital, but when Dave's mum had heard about it, she'd been in no doubt as to what the trouble was.

'Rubbish!' she'd said. 'You're pregnant, aren't you?'

Caroline had been dumbfounded. It had not occurred to her.

'Well, never mind,' Dave's mum had said. 'There'll be no problem about having an abortion, especially at your age. You'll be in and out in a jiffy, then you can just carry on as usual. Just be a bit more careful next time.'

They'd been sitting in the kitchen at Dave's parents' house, Dave and his parents and Caroline, over a Saturday afternoon cup of tea. There had been a moment of silence after this pronouncement. Dave, who had started in his chair at the news, his face draining of colour, had relaxed again, relieved. His mum had said, 'Well! I'll just refresh the pot,' and had got up. Dave and his dad had both looked at Caroline, who was sitting quietly, looking at her hands in her lap.

She'd looked up and said, 'No.'

'What?' Dave's mum had turned sharply from the sink where she'd been refilling the kettle, spilling water over the work surface.

'No, I can't.' Caroline had started to shake. 'I'm sorry! It's a *baby*. It's *my* baby.' She'd looked at Dave, pleadingly. '*Our* baby, Dave!'

Dave, speechless and white, had looked at his mum for guidance. She'd come back to the table and had sat down again, slowly.

'You can't have this baby, Caroline,' she'd said, very deliberately. 'You don't have any money, either of you, or a home, and you're much too young to know how to look after a baby. Dave needs to get on, not get tied down before he's even started. And what about all this studying you say you're so keen to do? You'll wreck both your lives. Don't be silly! You haven't had two minutes even to think about it.'

It was this conversation, and many subsequent ones, which Caroline was going over as she sat on the doorstep that cold October afternoon. Dave had vacillated between his mum and Caroline until his parents, angry and frustrated, had told him to leave. The bedsit was the best the council had been able to offer them, until something else came up.

To be fair it had been hard on Dave, Caroline acknowledged that. He hadn't wanted a baby; and torn between the pressures of his family, his girlfriend and his new job, he could never see which way to turn at any given moment. To be honest, he hadn't known Caroline that long; he hated living in squalor instead of the comfort of his parents' house with everything laid on; and he resented the claims made on him when what he really wanted was someone to look after *him.*

Caroline knew all this, and struggled herself with being too young, with having nobody but Dave to take care of her, and with having to learn everything the hard way. And sometimes, for all that she was brave and practical and got on with it because she had to, it was just too much.

She'd been so sure that having the baby was the right thing to do; but also she'd longed for someone who would be her very own, it was true. As she'd felt the growing life begin to move and kick inside her, she'd been overwhelmed with wonder. And when the baby had been born, when she'd been placed into Caroline's eager arms for the first time, Caroline had looked into her face and fallen hopelessly in love.

But she hadn't had any idea it would be so hard. It was the relentlessness of it all that was so wearing: *always* to be cleaning or cooking or doing some chore, never being able just to get up and do something because you felt like it. Never getting enough sleep.

And the trouble was, you could see things coming but you just didn't have the energy to do anything about them. She could see Dave didn't want to know; she could see his parents were keeping their distance. There was nobody to help her.

She leaned her face against the rotting doorframe and sobbed.

Dr Carr stopped typing and sat back in her chair. She was very tired. Her daughter Vicky, who taught Sociology at a difficult London comprehensive, had asked her to write a contribution for the school's magazine, which was running a series of stories on teenage problems. She'd said, 'You could do it on teenage pregnancy, couldn't you, Mum? But also will you give them your "imagine" bit, and something about your work, why you love it? You know, as an encouragement?'

There was so much to say and she'd rather put it off, and now she was close to her deadline. So she'd got up early to try and break the back of it before the day's work began. She realised that writing it like this, as a straight account, might not be the best way; however at least it got it down onto paper and she could fiddle with it later. She was hesitating over the 'imagine' bit, partly because of what might be happening later on today. As she thought about that, her eyes shone.

She glanced at her watch. It was just coming up to four, and still pitch black. Outside it would be hot and sticky, but it was cool in here, under the rotating ceiling fan. She was sitting at her desk at base HQ, in front of an oldish computer that nonetheless was enough for what she wanted. There was nothing else on the desk apart from a glass paperweight. She liked to work without clutter, but the paperweight was precious to her and she kept it with her always.

Dr Carr was a doctor with NERU, MSF's Nigerian emergency response unit. She loved it. From the moment she'd first heard about MSF she'd been enchanted by the concept of doctors without borders, simply going to where the need was greatest; and as soon as Vicky left school she had begun working with them in Africa – first in Angola, then Liberia and western Sudan. She'd become particularly interested in fighting epidemics, and the meningitis epidemic which had swept through the 'meningitis belt' from Senegal to Ethiopia over the last six months was the worst in thirteen years. You could do so much with so little: without treatment the death rate was around fifty per cent, yet most people would be cured with a single dose of antibiotics. Speed was vital, though, as the majority of deaths occurred within forty-eight hours; but also the numbers were huge, so the personnel had to move fast to cover the ground. It was the biggest vaccination campaign that MSF had ever carried out, and Dr Carr felt the privilege of being a part of it.

The teams would arrive at four thirty to start setting up for the day ahead – they'd probably do something like two and a half thousand vaccinations today. They'd leave at about five, arrive at the clinic at about six, and be vaccinating by seven. There was always a doctor with the teams to treat people who actually had meningitis, and to advise. That was her role, once she'd helped load up. As always, it would be a long day, and there was nowhere in the world she would rather be; but there would be no more writing-time today.

Dr Carr turned back to her keyboard. She didn't have long.

After a bit Caroline rubbed her eyes, dug around in her pocket for a tissue and wiped her nose, and listlessly looked up. She saw that Adeola from next door was trailing down the street towards her, holding something carefully in her hands. She stopped at the gap in the street-level railings from which four steep steps went down to the area where the basement doorway was, in which Caroline was sitting. When she saw Caroline she hesitated, then climbed carefully down the steps and came to sit beside her. Caroline shifted over for her.

Adeola was small for her age and was usually dressed in a variety of random clothes to try to keep her warm; that day she had on a flowery summer skirt which was hopeless for a rainy English October afternoon, a light blouse and some sort of sweater and a woman's sagging brown cardigan, and cheap plastic sandals on her bare feet. Caroline liked Adeola; she liked the little corkscrews her mum made all over her head with coloured rubber bands, her big dark eyes and her wide smile. On cue Adeola smiled at her, and she tried to smile back.

'Here,' said Adeola, putting something on her knee. 'For you, Caroline.'

Caroline looked. It was a large leaf. She had no idea what kind – maybe sycamore, maple? She didn't really care. The mix of yellow and orange autumn colours was pretty, though – more shining gold and copper, as it was wet. She didn't quite know what to do with it. A corner of it was folded over and there was a muddy streak across one end.

'What is it, Adeola?'

'A golden bird. For you.'

Caroline thought she'd misheard, but she was too miserable to ask again, so she just looked at the wet leaf. She was puzzled. Surely, Adeola had said 'a golden bird'? What on earth could she mean?

And then suddenly, Caroline saw it. The leaf's curved stalk formed the bird's legs, the folded part was the bird's round breast, and the shiny outer edges of the leaf gave the wings and tail. Caroline saw the raised beak and the unfolding gold-tipped wings, the rounded golden breast, the legs in the act of being tucked up for flight, the tail feathers. The muddy streak formed the shadows under the wings and, at one end, there was a final drip that made the eye. The ridge down the middle lifted the whole thing into a rounded shape, and Adeola was quite right – it was a shining golden bird in the moment after lift-off with the sun on it, soaring.

Adeola and Caroline stared at the bird. All around them was so wet, so cold and grey – but they were looking at a glowing bird, glinting in the sun.

Dr Carr stopped typing. Through the fug of tiredness she searched for words that would do justice to the moment when the imagination springs to life for the first time. She typed:

A dead leaf that is both a dead leaf and a living bird taught Caroline that things aren't always what they seem at first sight. Moreover, that even something that seems dead can carry within itself the living substance of something else: a promise that can be grasped and held.

As she stared at the leaf which was also bird, it seemed to Caroline that all natural things were made of the same stuff, and that if only you knew how to look, you would be able to discover what is common to them all. The thirst for knowledge, and more, the longing to put that knowledge to fruitful use, sprang to life in her with a force that made her gasp.

Suddenly the world was huge. She felt that it was opening up before her astonished gaze. In such a world, anything was possible.

Caroline said, 'Adeola, what do you want to be when you grow up?'

'A teacher,' said Adeola promptly, 'like Miss Kirkpatrick at my school. She's nice. If we have to go back to Katsina I could tell the children there everything she has taught us.'

'Did she teach you how to see a bird in a leaf?'

'Sort of. She is always telling us to look carefully, because the world is so beautiful.'

They both stared at the bright, wet leaf. Caroline said, 'She's right. It really is, isn't it?'

'Yes,' said Adeola. 'What are you going to be, Caroline?'

Caroline heard herself say, 'I'm going to be a doctor.' And, for the first time, she believed it.

Dr Carr stopped and stretched. It was a good place to stop, so she logged off. It was almost time. She'd have to leave till tomorrow the rest of Caroline's story – how she'd got herself a part-time book-keeping job at the local car showroom, and how, even though Dave had moved out, his parents, belatedly, had taken an interest in their first grandchild and had looked after her twice a week during those early years, until Caroline had been able to find neighbours and friends with whom she could share joint childcare arrangements. How she'd gone to night school. How she'd become an expert on grants, bursaries, any source of funding. How she'd done all kinds of jobs to make up the difference. How she'd got there in the end.

And how, every time she hadn't known what to do or had felt alone, she'd looked at Adeola's leaf to remind herself that the world was big and full of wonders, and that there was always somebody around the corner who would help her. So far, whenever she had looked for that person, she had never failed to find them.

As Dr Carr stood up there was a knock, the door opened and Richard came in. Richard was a medical student and this was his third stint as a volunteer with the unit. He and Dr Carr had worked together before, and got on well. She smiled at him.

'Morning, Richard. All set?'

He nodded. 'Teams are just rolling in now.'

'Good, I'll get along then.' She reached across the desk, picked up the paperweight and slipped it into her pocket. 'See you down there,' she said, and left.

Richard gazed after her. He adored Dr Carr, and thought she was the best doctor on the unit. She was quick and professional, but had the unerring knack of being able to pick out those who needed more time and those who needed smoothly to be moved on. It was an education to watch her dealing with these without their ever realising what she was doing. She was unfailingly kind with children and the elderly, who were often afraid; and she never assumed anything without first taking the time to make sure she fully understood, which had often saved a lot of trouble.

He loved how she travelled extremely light and never seemed to have anything with her that wouldn't fit into her modest backpack, which left her hands free to carry other things as needed. While being perfectly friendly and open, she spoke little and to the point, which was restful. And you knew you could rely on her absolutely, that she wouldn't have any domestic emergencies or personal dramas for which the team would have to make allowances. Hearing her on the phone once to her daughter, he'd asked Dr Carr who looked after her while she was away on duty, and Dr Carr had smiled and said 'Vicky's twenty-five and looks after herself very effectively,' which had astounded him, as Dr Carr barely looked older than that herself; but she'd just grinned at him and hadn't elaborated.

So when this tour of duty had taken the unit to Katsina, Richard had been curious to hear Dr Carr asking the teams to look out for a particular name on the vaccination tally sheets, and to tell her if it came up; and thrilled that, the previous afternoon, he'd been the one to be able to bring her some news. He'd been looking over the day's sheets and had said to his colleague who'd been checking them, 'No Adeola today again, then?' And a woman who was in the queue had said, 'The teacher? Oh, she's coming tomorrow, she's bringing the children.'

When he'd reported this to Dr Carr at the end of the day, she'd stopped dead, the box she was carrying halfway into the back of the van she was loading up. He'd watched the light in her eyes grow from deep within. 'Bringing the children?' she'd said. 'Of course, so she would be.'

He hoped he'd be around to see this Adeola, and that he'd find out what it was all about. But meanwhile, he was disappointed that Dr Carr had taken the paperweight with her, because he'd been hoping to sneak another look at it.

Dr Carr always worked at a clear desk, but that paperweight was always on it. Curious, he'd once picked it up when she was out of the room, feeling guilty; it was very plain, just a thick rectangular slab of glass with something brown and very thin inside. He'd held it up to the light. How odd; the brown something looked sort of torn and irregular and had, he thought, lines like veins in it, but he couldn't work out what it could be. Hurriedly he'd put the paperweight back, but the brown thing had nagged at him, so he'd looked for an opportunity to steal another quick look. However, on this tour the paperweight had only been on the desk when Dr Carr herself had been in the room, and he'd felt embarrassed about asking.

As he slowly closed the door behind him he wondered, for the umpteenth time, what on earth it was.

4. Amy's Visit

FORGIVE

'Then Peter came to Jesus and asked, "Lord, how many times shall I forgive my brother when he sins against me? Up to seven times?" Jesus answered, "I tell you, not seven times, but seventy-seven times."'
Matthew 18:21-22

FRIDAY, APRIL 3rd

For a week or two after the clocks have changed, if you go to the park late in the afternoon the board at the entrance still says 'This park will close at 6pm', which it did before the clocks went forward. But now, who knows what time it closes? Not at six, anyway. I know. I go there at about ten past six and the place is deserted, but it's still sunny, it's lovely. All the rest of the time it's full of people and dogs and babies and pushchairs, but after six there's only me. Even on a Friday, like today.

I sit on my bench and I feel safe. The park is only a few yards from home and the bench is only a hundred yards in. I won't go further. You go in through the gates and across an open car park area and then the ground sweeps down to the lake. My bench is on the grass just beyond the car park gravel, before the ground dips. There's another bench to the left and before this one, but there's a big tree behind it, someone could come up behind you and you wouldn't know.

Whereas my bench is clear all around, nobody could be anywhere near without my seeing, and I'm fast. I know I could run clear in time, and the gate's only a hundred yards away.

SATURDAY, APRIL 4th

Of course it isn't my bench really. It says along the back '"Oma" there at our beginning, we will love her till our end'. Tom and I called our German grandad 'Opa', so I know Oma must be the grandma of the people who put the bench here. You can tell they loved her. I feel as if she was my Oma too, as if the arms of the bench are her arms around me, making that safe circle of beginning and end. Nobody can hurt me here.

Of course you can never be quite *quite* sure, so I always sit at an angle in the far corner of the bench – that way I can keep an eye on anything behind me as well as look down to the lake.

There are ducks and geese and moorhens and swans, and at this time they're usually settled on the grass all around the edge with their beaks under their wings. It's so beautiful, so still. All the little boats and pedalos are safely moored up to the pontoon until tomorrow, red and blue and green and yellow, with the different-sized lifejackets hanging on the rack outside the wooden shed where they sell the tickets. Oh, how I'd love to go on one of those little boats!

From time to time when he visits Tom offers to take me, and I do feel safe with Tom, but even so – I just can't. Sometimes when he comes he sits with me on my bench. He used to encourage me to go to the park earlier, when there are other people about, to get me used to them, he said; we could walk down together to look at the little boats. So once I did go with him an hour earlier than usual, but we had to come straight back. I do feel safe with Tom, but not that safe.

Maybe if Mum or Dad were still around it would be different. But since everything fell apart after what happened to me, since they got divorced and then eventually both sort of stopped coming to see me after I ended up here in the home, I'll never know.

Tom's a good kind brother, but he doesn't understand. How could he? I don't understand either, and I remember so little of what happened.

MONDAY, APRIL 6th

Today I had a new counsellor. Her name is Jen. They keep making me see a counsellor even though I say I don't see the point, so now I just don't say anything. If counsellors want to sit there for an hour, let them.

It's pretty boring. We meet in the Annexe which has no windows, just a big skylight, and apart from two chairs and a small table and a cupboard there's nothing else in the room.

They put on that sickly counsellor face which makes me want to throw something at them. Sometimes they sit back, all exaggerated-relaxed as if they'd just dropped by for a coffee, and sometimes they sit forward and try to engage with me, but either way they don't talk normally and I hate it. When they ask me something it always feels loaded with some kind of code that I don't know – as if it's a game or competition where they know the rules and I don't, where anything I say will be used in ways I didn't mean. I don't trust them. Why should I say anything? So I don't.

But Jen's different. She's sort of calm inside and she just sits quietly with her knees and feet together and her hands in her lap, and she doesn't try to make me do anything. At the beginning when she introduced herself and explained what she was there for, she just spoke normally – just the words, no code. I was surprised. It was nice – sort of detached-friendly. She said that this was my time so I could do whatever I wanted with it, and after she finished talking and invited me to say something, and I didn't, she just sat with me. She didn't put on the counsellor face and she seemed to be happy just to sit with me for ever, if that's what I wanted. She had a way of sitting with me that was *with* me – nobody was saying anything but I knew that she was paying attention to me all the time. I've never been with anyone like that before.

MONDAY, APRIL 20th
Jen just sits. It's quite peaceful, but it's an odd feeling.

MONDAY, APRIL 27th
Today I said to her 'I wonder what you're thinking.'

She smiled and said 'I was wondering the same thing about you.'

I said 'I don't know. I suppose, whether you'd like my park.'

She said 'Tell me about your park, Amy,' so I did. I told her about Oma and the little boats and the grass that sweeps down to the water, and the peacefulness. It was just chatting, just normal, it was nice. And I knew she understood because she said 'And what about when people adjust to the clocks going forward and stay later?' And I sort of ducked my head the way I do and I said 'Well, I have to pay attention, I kind of monitor it, I go later and later. Sometimes I can't stay, but mostly there's some time at the very end of the day, even if it's just a little bit.'

And she said 'That's good,' and I felt happy.

TUESDAY, APRIL 28th
I only remember the window. That's all – just the window, so high up. I know it was a sunny day because the window was a big square of bright blue. It was shut and I couldn't reach it. If I could have reached it, if I could have opened it, I could have got away.

WEDNESDAY, MAY 20th
I know Jen has seen my file, my notes. There must be a lot in there. I could ask to see them if I wanted, but I don't. What's the point? Up till now, anyway. Up till now I haven't cared what the counsellors put. But I wonder what Jen puts? I would like Jen to be able to put something that is real.

SUNDAY, JUNE 21st
Tom came to see me today and stayed to lunch. It's been such a lovely day, and after lunch we walked in the garden a bit. The garden's quite large but it's plain and neat – just a large grassy rectangle really, there isn't anywhere to go in it, so we just sat on a bench and talked. Tom's paper sent him to Paris a few months ago so I haven't seen him for a while. I was asking him about what he was writing and whether he liked it better being a journalist over there than here, and he suddenly looked at me and said 'Amy, you've never asked me about my work before,' and I thought, no I haven't, it's true. He smiled and said 'It feels good to tell you about it,' and I said 'It feels good to hear about it,' and I was surprised, because that was true too.

MONDAY, JUNE 29th
Today was an amazing day.

There was such a blue sky today when Jen came. We were in the Annexe as usual and the skylight was bright blue, not a cloud anywhere. I said to Jen 'It's like the window the day it happened, it was just like that,' and she said 'Would you like to tell me about it, Amy?' And I wanted to, it felt fine to tell Jen. But I couldn't because I can't remember.

So Jen said 'Start at the beginning.'

I said 'Okay, I was eight. I was off school with a temperature and a sore throat, but Mum had made me up a bed downstairs in the sitting room.'

'Do you remember that?'

'No. But she told me. I don't remember anything.'

'Okay,' Jen said. 'Go on.'

'Then she went to get Tom from school and I asked if I could stay at home, and she left the door to the back garden open, it was a lovely day and she was only going to be twenty minutes.'

I sort of stopped then, because nobody was there when he came apart from me. So of course if I don't remember, then nobody knows what happened, exactly.

Jen waited a bit and then she said gently 'What did your mum say happened after that?'

'They came home, Mum and Tom. They thought I was dead, there was so much blood.' There's something I've never understood, and now Jen was here and I suddenly thought, she might explain it to me. I said 'He had a knife and he cut me everywhere, on my face and my hands and my arms, I have scars' – I touched my face, but of course she can see – 'and he cut me inside too, I had lots of operations.'

Jen was just looking at me, just listening. She didn't look upset, she was paying attention, so I simply asked her what's always bothered me.

'So how come I don't remember anything? How could anyone forget something so important?'

Jen leaned forward and said 'Amy, your mind is amazingly powerful and its job is to protect you. It will bury something that might be too terrible for a little girl to remember. But when you're grown up, if you want to enough and if you're willing to work at it with someone who can help, you can heal what happened to the little you.'

I was really surprised. I said 'What, you mean always?'

'Absolutely.'

'You mean bad things can always be healed? *Any* bad thing, even if it's really, really bad?'

Jen looked at me very straight and she said 'I'm quite sure that there is nothing, nothing at all that is beyond recovery, as long as the people involved are willing to work through it. It will never be easy and it may take a long time, but if they're willing, then yes. *Any* bad thing can be healed.'

I must have stared at Jen for a long time.

MONDAY, SEPTEMBER 7th

I haven't written anything for weeks and weeks, but today I looked back and I'll try to fill in the missing bits, because today has been really important too, just like the day when I last wrote anything.

Jen thought that the window was my way in. I can remember that window perfectly – it had a white wooden surround and two big panes, side by side, which opened outwards from the centre – two big slabs of blue. And each window had a brass handle to open it, only someone had painted over the little plates with the screws when they painted the woodwork. I knew that each window opened just fine, though, I knew that whenever I stood on one of the two chairs that were against the wall underneath, I could reach easily.

Not that day, though.

And now I have no other memories of that window, before or after – just that one, that day, so high up, so far away, so bright, bright blue.

Jen suggested a reconstruction. She explained how she could lead me back to that day in my mind so that I can act out a different outcome – get up, open the window, climb out and run away. I couldn't do that then, but I can do it now. I can give an old memory a new ending. The grown-up me can rescue the little me.

I'm not sure how it could work but I trust Jen, and now I'm getting excited. But I'm scared, too. Will it mean I remember what happened? Jen says maybe I will and maybe I won't, but she'll be with me and she'll guide me – I won't be by myself like I was then. She says she'll lead me in and lead me out again, back to now, and that the thing to remember is that, whatever happens, I'm living now, not then.

So today we went to see if there is any room here where we can do this. The Annexe won't work since it only has a skylight. It has to feel to me like it felt then, even if it doesn't actually look the same.

And we found the perfect place. The window in the computer room is a big double window, really high up, and both sides open outwards from the centre, and have the same kind of handle to open them, although these are plastic. It's higher than the real one was – I'm taller now. But if I put two chairs under that double window I'll reach easily, just like when I was little.

It's an L-shaped room and round the corner is a door to the outside. And on the other side of both the door and the window, just like at home when I was young, is the garden.

We're doing it next week.

MONDAY, SEPTEMBER 14th

I can't describe it. I can't say what happened. But we did it, we did it, and everything's changed.

FRIDAY, SEPTEMBER 18th

I only want to say some parts – it's too soon for all of it.

I was lying on the floor and there was no pain and no awareness of any other person being there, only an overwhelming sensation of being paralysed. Jen's voice said 'What are you feeling, Amy?' And I said 'There's a really, really heavy weight pressing down, I can't move.'

Jen said 'Do you want to move?'

And I said 'Yes, I want to run away,' and she said 'Tell me how you can do that.' And I said 'I can open the window and climb out,' and she said 'Okay, when you're ready, go ahead. Get up, open the window and leave.'

Somehow it was very simple and I didn't even think of anything particular, I just got up. But as I did that I suddenly thought, I'm twenty-four years old. I'm twenty-four and I'm fit and well and I'm climbing out of the window because I *can*. And I stepped up onto the chair and took hold of the handle of the right-hand window and turned it. The window swung open. I pulled myself up, pushed with my feet and dropped onto the grass below.

Jen must have shot through the door because she was already in the garden when I touched the ground and started running.

MONDAY, SEPTEMBER 21st

We have a really good gym in the house and I go there every day. I've always said to myself it will never happen to me again because next time I will be strong and fast and I will get away. I've always sort of known that there would be a next time, that one day I would have to run. What I didn't realise was that when that day came, it would be a day I'd already lived.

I ran round and round the big square garden because that's where I was, but it was the running that mattered not the place, I was eight and there was a man and I needed to get away. I don't know how long it took. I only stopped when it just wasn't possible to run any more.

And then I urgently needed to find the safe place that I knew was there, and I reached for it, for Jen. I don't remember how I got there, but I finished curled up on her lap on the grass with her arms around me tight, as I cried and cried and cried and cried and cried.

MONDAY, SEPTEMBER 28th

I haven't remembered any more. Jen says it clearly wasn't necessary for me to remember. I'm glad.

I'm different inside. It's as if the running has freed me and the crying has washed me. It's as if I used to be tied up in a filthy dark dungeon, and now somebody has cut the ropes and taken me out into the light and given me a hot bath. I can move. I can do whatever I want to do. I am free to go.

I can't stop touching things, I stand in the rain when it rains, I walk around the garden feeling leaves and bark and petals and grass, I sit on the ground crumbling clumps of earth in my hands. Last week someone came in with a dog and he wagged his tail and came towards me. One of the helpers started to intervene and I said no, no, and knelt down to hug him and he licked my ear and I burst into tears.

But the very best time was yesterday, when Tom came. I was waiting for him in the hall. When he came through the door I ran towards him, and his face lit up and he opened his arms and I went straight into them. It was the best, *best* hug! Now I know what my brother feels like, his back and his shoulders and his hands. We both cried and held each other and he stroked my hair and my face and kept saying my name: Amy, Amy.

MONDAY, OCTOBER 19th

I keep thinking about the man who hurt me. I get great surges of rage, anger, terror. Sometimes I just start crying for no reason and can't stop. Why did he do it? *Why?*

Jen helps. We work though it each time. She shows me ways of working through it by myself when she's not there, but I can phone her too, and sometimes I do that. And it's true, it comes in great waves and then it goes, I have to sit tight and it *will* go! But each time it comes, I can work through a little more.

But I'm so, *so* tired.

MONDAY, NOVEMBER 16th

Jen talks about time a lot, and how time passing really does heal. She keeps reminding me that I'm living now, not then, which is why I can do this. I'm grown up now. *I* can take responsibility for me.

MONDAY, NOVEMBER 30th

Today I realised something. I can choose: to stay in the darkness, or to turn from that darkness and walk forwards into light. I can hold onto what happened to me, or I can put it down. Only I can choose, but also, I can't help choosing, I choose anyway. So, what do I choose?

I choose to turn: I choose to live: the scars are there, but they are old.

MONDAY, DECEMBER 7th

His name is Martin Jones. I think he will be nearing the end of his prison sentence soon.

I talk to Jen about him. She asked me today how I felt about him, and I said I don't know, sort of empty. But actually what I mostly feel is that I would like to understand. And now I'm not in prison any more, and he still is.

That was such a strange thing to think. As if we're sort of linked, as if there is a shared connection.

This thing happened to *us*, not just to me.

I don't know what to feel. But I don't hate him.

WEDNESDAY, DECEMBER 9th

I don't blame him either. It's so strange.

I said to Jen 'I suppose I would like him to know that I'm not in prison any more because of what he did.'

Jen said 'Would you?'

I said 'Yes. Maybe it would help him.'

Jen said 'How would that make *you* feel?'

I thought about it. I said 'I think it makes me feel free.'

MONDAY, JANUARY 11th

The strangest thing happened today. So strange because of all I've been thinking.

I received a letter, a letter from the probation office in Garden Road. They say that Martin Jones is coming to the end of his sentence and that he would like to write to me. They say that he has come to 'regret deeply' what he did and that he wishes to ask my forgiveness. They are confident that his regret is genuine because of all the work he has done in recent months, especially on a rehabilitation programme during which he wrote a letter for me. They ask how I would feel about receiving such a letter?

I said I would like to have it. I would like to read it here, with Jen.

MONDAY, SEPTEMBER 13th

That letter was the beginning. After that I knew, and I think he knew too, that we would like to meet. Forgiveness has to be something mutual, to be asked for and received in person, together. How else can we reach towards the previous occasion on which we were together?

It took such a long time and there was so much preparation involved.

But today, this afternoon, we met.

It was in the prison chapel and it was a little octagonal room, with a big cross on a red background behind an altar, blue chairs, a wooden floor, plain, clean, ordinary. He had his personal officer and a chaplain with him, and I had Tom and Jen. When we came in and they stood up, the room felt full of people.

I thought he would be big, tall, strong. He's sixty-three, he isn't old.

But he was small. When he stood up and turned towards me, I saw he had watery eyes and a dry, grey face. He looked very much older than sixty-three. He had a cough.

He sparked no memories. I had to remind myself why I was here, to see this stranger. Somehow I had been so sure that I would feel the connection that I had thought was there.

We just looked at each other. I put out my hand, to shake his. He took it and looked at it. I'm right-handed, and my right hand is the worse one of the two.

He looked at my hand and then he looked up at my face, and he said 'I did that. Didn't I? I did that.'

And that's when I felt the connection. He'd been in my story all this time after all, this man I couldn't remember; only now I knew who he was.

I was overwhelmed by sadness. He looked so defeated, frail, spent.

It wasn't difficult to take his hand, to smile at him. I said 'Yes. But the scars are old. I'm all right now.'

THURSDAY, SEPTEMBER 16th

I keep thinking about him. About all we said on Monday. About all there is still to say.

But today I'm mostly thinking about Saturday.

On Saturday, Tom's coming. And we're going to the park. First we'll sit on Oma's bench, and then we'll walk down to the lake together and go on a little boat.

Tom said, 'How about one of those pedalos, you know, the two-person ones?'

But I think I'll choose a little rowing boat – a little sky-blue one – all of my very own.

5. Jack's Gift

SEE WHAT IS THERE

'The eye is the lamp of the body. If your eyes are good, your whole body will be full of light. But if your eyes are bad, your whole body will be full of darkness. If then the light within you is darkness, how great is that darkness!'
Matthew 6:22-23

It was early on a grey Saturday morning in December, but the shopping centre was already busy. Shoals of people pressed along the wide central spaces, eddying around benches and bins, chattering, excited, nervous. They pulled toddlers behind them or pushed pushchairs, hurrying past strangers, executing odd little sideways avoidance dances, rushing between shops as if they had no time, eyes blank like fish bobbing on a tide, or intent, confused, even desperate. It would soon be Christmas.

It was too early for the older children who, later, with their mums or grandads, would sit on the benches swinging their legs and sharing ice creams and pretzels; too early too for the brittle teenagers whose idle, casual appearance belied the care that went into creating it and whose shrill laughter would jump, by lunchtime, from one gaudy flock to another. This was the serious time, the 'I'll just nip in before it gets busy' time, the time of the grim shopper.

Paul was the stallholder in the top corner (between handbags – 'new stock every week!', and innovations – 'gifts for every occasion!'), and he usually set up about now. He did it out of habit, though he sold so little now it was barely worth it. What else could he do? He knew nothing else, and he was honest, and proud. As long as he could just about scrape a living he wouldn't go on the dole.

But it was more than that. In some dogged place deep inside, he knew his worth; he was good, he was! It was what kept him going. He wouldn't give up, he'd go on trying, at least.

Mechanically he set out his wares, and as always the sight of them flooded his heart with bitterness and rage. He'd loved these things once, once they'd been precious and marvellous, but now! Now he could barely sell any, and nothing, anywhere, had meaning for him any more. He was consumed with hopeless grief and fed on it, agonisingly – reliving, over and over, the short life of joy he'd once had, as if it were a film, or had happened to someone else. Certainly, now, it had nothing to do with him.

He would be attractive to look at, if anyone ever did look: tall, slim, dark, still young, with long legs and wide shoulders, a straight nose, an expressive mouth. But people hurried past him because the intensity of his despair was almost menacing – it was as if the black cloud that wrapped him round was contagious and they wanted to give him a wide berth. He frightened them. His whole body seemed to be hunched, dark, coiled in on itself.

Sometimes a child saw something lovely on his stall and called out, but Paul was used to women pulling their children away now and no longer reacted or called after them, as he sometimes had before. In those early days of being on his own he couldn't understand it – he and Sal had been so busy always!

People used to swarm to the stand when they'd run it together, like ants to honey, drawn by her warmth. Oh she was lovely, was Sal – she would shake the long blond hair out of her face like a lion, drawing you to her with her happy laughing eyes, her soft voice with the slight Cornish burr transforming everything she said into a caress. Paul remembered her pleasure in the beautiful things he had made, her excited anticipation of what the day would bring, her sparkle.

They'd always done well – usually they had sold out by teatime (once, in the early inexperienced days, by lunchtime); they'd taken commissions for the following week and he'd been as busy as a squirrel, from one Saturday to the next, as wonders had taken shape under his astonished gaze.

For Paul was a toymaker of genius. Untutored and self-taught, he had an understanding of different woods that was uncanny, and could somehow see the possibility of any piece that came under his sensitive, seeking fingers. With eyes half-closed, his mind utterly relaxed, he would stroke and feel the wood, turning it over and over in his hands, aware of every turn of the grain, the shape of every knot and bump. To him it was a living thing, and when he carved it, he simply released what was already there.

Early on he had become fascinated by the way creatures move, and endlessly watched wildlife programmes until he had learned absolutely the spring of a lion, the fluid rush of a cheetah's run. Then he worked on different methods of reproducing these movements in the toys he made – one for a horse, one for an elephant, one for a goose.

Over the long hours of weeks and months he devised extraordinary mechanisms with string and bolts, pulleys and clamps, which reproduced the movement he wanted when the string was pulled. He sought clean simplicity: he could spend hours just looking at a mechanical problem, his mind empty, suspended; and all at once the answer would slide into place as neatly as one of his own devices, perfect.

And the care he took in painting them! He went to zoos to study fur and feathers, colours and textures – the rough, the silky, the finest tones of shading. And later, when he branched out into clowns and tramps, musicians and gymnasts, he devised ingenious structures for them, too – as well as costumes and balls and trumpets and hats.

Sal was as excited as he was as each new toy took shape. She sewed trousers and smocks and jackets, and because Paul loved every aspect of the work, she taught him the delicate stitching, the way to cut and fit things. Her delight in his work thrilled him and her pride in him was like hot chocolate in his tummy, a deep sweet well of joy. She was all he could ever have wanted or dreamed of. Everything he was, everything he could ever become, was rooted in her. His deep eyes shone with love and passers-by, irresistibly drawn by the wide curve of his happy smile, stayed to buy his toys, and told their friends.

There are still people who visit the shopping centre now who knew Paul then, and who occasionally (as they hurry past) wonder what happened to the young man with the extraordinary talent and the glowing young wife, who used to have that stand.

'Remember, Shirl?' one will say to another. 'They was such a nice young couple!'

'Yes, so happy! And him – remember that giraffe I got Connor? You would swear he was real, he was that good, remember?'

'And the horse I got for Dan, and Kayleigh's little clown – course I remember! Such a shame they went away, them things was beautiful.'

'You don't see toys that quality any more.'

'No, for sure. And that miserable geezer who took over with his rubbish, he gives me the creeps.'

When Sal was alive it was grand – it was. But when she died he lost all his world. He had no means of understanding the darkness that engulfed him or the terror of his days. The stand stayed empty for months, he couldn't bear even to think of it. And when Sal died not only did he lose her, he gained a millstone round his neck.

Jack!

When he'd been a baby Sal had cut and stitched with Jack tucked up beside her in the armchair; he'd been content to watch the flash of her needle, and she had let him stroke the dappled flank of the painted horse, the sweet-sad smile of the clown.

When he was a little older she had shown him the intricate designs of the mechanisms inside, and how to activate them by pulling the toys' strings. She had taught him a sense of wonder, and to touch things gently.

There hadn't been time to teach him anything else. The cancer that killed her claimed her after only three short months. After that, Paul and Jack were on their own.

And as if that wasn't enough, Paul had thought resentfully a thousand times, Jack turned out stupid. A 'learning disability' they called it, and he had to go to a special place, not to proper school like other children. Paul raged against losing both his wife and his son. Sal would have known what to do with him; he knew that with Sal there, Jack would somehow have been all right.

As it was, Paul fell into bitterness and despair. What was the use, what was the good, of anything? He raged at Sal for abandoning him, even though he knew it was unreasonable. He couldn't help himself. He would sit in his workshop for hours, doing nothing. Soon there was nothing to do anyway – even after he returned to the abandoned stand (what else could he do?), people avoided the dark, brooding man with the brightly-coloured toys, and he sold very little.

When Jack was small he'd had to take the lad with him, of

course. He was a quiet boy, Paul gave him that, but what was the use of him? Paul made very sure he never touched the toys, he was sure to break them, clumsy fool that he was. So Jack just sat and watched, for hours. It was unnatural, Paul thought angrily. If only he'd had a proper son, who could have helped him in his business, as other men had! As soon as he decently could, he left Jack at home. He looked so like his mother Paul could hardly bear the sight of him.

And that was the nub of it, really. To see Sal at every turn as the lad grew – the shape of her mouth, her dear-remembered eyes in a different face – was almost unbearable; and yet to see her even like this was better than not seeing her at all. To see her in Jack day by day twisted the knife of his pain and kept his grief raw. He clung to the memory of his skill and to the sunny features that he loved, bound together as they had always been for him. And he was stuck.

And so it went on until that grey December Saturday when Paul, not paying attention, slipped in the rain on his way home and broke his ankle. Jack was seventeen. A bad break, they said at the hospital as they plastered it up; he was to keep his foot up and not use it at all for six weeks.

'You'll have to take the stand to the shopping centre instead,' Paul said to Jack that night. 'Can't be helped, just have to do the best you can. Try not to break anything! I'll price it all up, you can't do too much damage, after all.'

'You mean take the toys, to the shops, to sell?' Jack was incredulous.

'Yes! What else can I do? We have to try to earn a living, at least! And I'll put the prices on everything, you just have to put them out – '

'But Da, what about the money? I can't do the change and that, I'm slow – '

'You're hardly likely to sell anything, now are you, I barely sell anything myself, so that won't be a problem. Just – just do what you can. I suppose you can't help it,' Paul added reluctantly.

The following Monday there was excitement in the shopping centre.

'Oh, Betty, do come and look! There's a new stand up with just marvellous toys, they'll be perfect for Christmas, for the grandchildren! Do look!'

'But what's happened to that awful chap, the one with the nasty gaudy stuff?'

'Don't know, but these are lovely, look!'

Jack stood in a haze of love and joy, surrounded by wonders. For as long as he could remember he had dreamed of holding in his hands his father's beautiful creatures, and now he had them all to himself, for a whole day! He lovingly took them out of their boxes and arranged them as he had seen his father do many times, and then he just walked around the stand, pulling softly on this string and on that, watching the lion spring, the cheetah run, the horse gallop. He was oblivious to the curious glances of passers-by who, arrested by the trembling stillness of his attentive gaze, followed his eyes to see what he was looking at and were, in their turn, captivated. His face suffused with a shy tenderness, he gently stroked the dappled flank of the horse as the shadow of a memory glimmered of someone kind and warm. He cradled a jaunty clown in his receptive hands, following with his finger the detail of the tiny stitching. He pulled the string, and laughed delightedly as it performed a perfect cartwheel.

'Oh, let me see! Show me!'

Jack smiled at the little girl pulling on his arm, and put the clown on the floor for her. But to his surprise there were lots of people around the stand now, and they all wanted to see different things – the bear, the acrobat, the gazelle. 'How much?' they all said, 'how much is this?'

'I don't know,' said Jack anxiously, the light in his face dying. 'The prices will be on there, I'm not sure – '

'Do you have change for a twenty?'

Jack opened his father's cashbox and showed the lady the meagre contents. 'I don't know – '

The lady smiled at him. 'Keep the change, son,' she said, kindly. 'This is cheap at the price. Happy Christmas!'

'Happy Christmas!' replied Jack belatedly as she walked away.

It was a busy morning.

Shortly after lunchtime Paul attempted to hobble upstairs with the aid of his crutch – no mere break was going to get the better of him, and he needed the bathroom – before settling with having to make the journey ignominiously, backwards on his bottom, with the crutch to help with leverage.

He was not in the best of tempers therefore when, just as he was emerging from the bathroom and considering the return journey, the front door banged open and Jack stumbled in, breathless.

'Da! Da! You'll have to make some more!'

'What?'

'Look!' Jack opened the cashbox and emptied it onto the floor – a tumble of coloured notes and a clattering waterfall of leaping, spinning coins. 'I waited till I sold the last one! It didn't matter that I couldn't do the money, they said keep the change, or took what they needed by themselves! I sold them all, Da!'

There was a long pause. It took Jack, head flung back and laughing with pride and excitement, a moment to realise that all was not well. The sparkle in his eyes faded.

'Da – ?'

'Get up here.' Paul's face was thunderous.

'What, Da? Wasn't that right? I thought that was right – ' Jack walked slowly up the stairs to his father, a wary, watchful look beginning in his eyes. He stopped in front of him, on the cramped landing.

'Where did you get all that money?'

'I told you, Da, I sold the toys – '

'Don't be stupid, nobody buys those toys any more, you know that! Where are they? Have you thrown them away? They mattered to me! And there's a ton of money down there! What did you do, steal it? Where did you steal it from?'

Utterly bewildered, Jack tried to answer the barrage of questions. 'No – Da – I sold them, like you said – only some people gave me more, they said they were worth it – and look – ' Jack dug in his pocket and took out a little rectangle of card, 'there was this man, see, he said who made the toys and I said my Da, and he said to call him, he has toyshops, he said – '

Beside himself, Paul grabbed his son's shirt and pulled him towards him, and all the pent-up rage of all the years, all the sorrow and pain, erupted in a roar of anguish.

'You – you – how *dare* you! I thought things were bad enough, I thought nothing could get worse, ever! *Useless* – and *stupid* – and *thick* – ' on each word Paul bashed Jack against the wall – 'but now, a thief – and a liar – to boot! Oh *God!*' In his despair Paul let Jack go and pushed him roughly away. Dazed, Jack stumbled against the bannister and then, slowly and horribly, fell backwards down the stairs.

For a heartbeat Paul stood frozen in horror and then, abruptly sitting down on the top step, flung the crutch over the bannister rail and half slid, half tumbled down the stairs, grabbing the bannister supports as he went. At the bottom he hung onto the newel post, squatted on his good leg and looked.

Jack was lying sprawled on his back with his eyes closed, half up against the opposite wall of the narrow hallway. He'd cut his lip, which was bleeding; but Paul couldn't see blood anywhere else. Was he breathing? Paul listened: yes he was, and as Paul heard the slow breath in and out, he also saw Jack's chest rise and fall. Jack's face in repose was exactly like his mother's.

Paul studied it. Exactly like? No, in fact. Jack had his mother's mouth and eyes, and his thick tawny hair was just like hers. But the shape of his face was different. His nose was different, too. And he had a young man's soft stubble on different skin which was less fair.

As Paul identified the ways in which Jack was not Sal, it was as if Sal disengaged herself from her son and stood, fleetingly, apart. For a long, still moment Paul saw her quite clearly as she had been in life: vibrant, present, whole. And then the image faded.

Paul leant his face against the bannister and wept.

He knew, now, that she was gone. In all the raging and grief of the years since she had died, there had been no single moment in which he had allowed that truth in; as if by sheer opposition he could somehow have made it not so, somehow have prevented it and brought her back.

But now the fact of her absence settled on his spirit like nightfall on a summer's evening. There was nothing he could do; he could fight and fight until he killed himself and it would make no difference: she was gone, and he had to let her go.

It was some time before Paul felt how cold he was. Every bit of him ached, as if he'd been beaten all over. His face was wet, and he rubbed at it with the heels of his hands. Slowly, he opened his eyes, and looked up.

Jack hadn't moved, but his eyes were open and he was watching him.

Paul returned Jack's level look, slowly taking him in. It was as if he'd never seen him before. He licked his dry lips.

'Jack,' he said.

6. The Phone Call

LIVE IN THE PRESENT

'I tell you, now is the time of God's favour,
now is the day of salvation.'
2 Corinthians 6:2b

I used to love to hear your voice.

Even now, I could lift the phone out of its socket, dial your number and press 'call'. There would be a pause; then the sound that told me that your phone was ringing: one ring; two; three; four. Abruptly that last ring would be broken, I'd hear your intake of breath and my heart would leap as you spoke your name.

A moment earlier you might have been reading a novel perhaps, or cooking something exotic outside on your terrace barbeque, or splashing about in your pool; I wouldn't know: your 'now' would have been running parallel to mine, but I wouldn't have had a part in it.

Not, that is, until I dialled your number here in Tonbridge and, ten thousand miles away in Sydney, you answered me. At that instant your 'now' would tumble into mine, and it would become our 'now'; as it has so often done before.

It could be like that again. All I have to do is pick up the phone: I could summon you, like Aladdin rubbing his lamp. Or like one child saying to another, 'Will you play with me?'

Your number hasn't changed. I know that because of the Christmas card that faithfully falls on the mat every year with your contact details and brief news update. You have always made sure that, if I wanted to, I could find you again.

I remember your voice so well: light and clear, younger than your years, mixing a bit of Yorkshire from your parents, traces of a favourite Scottish teacher whose name I can't now remember, and, later, the more relaxed diction of your adopted country.

It used to tell me lots of things: I would know whether you'd just languidly extended a hand to pick up the phone from your armchair, or whether you'd heaved yourself out of the water, scooped a towel off the lounger to dry your hands, and walked across the deck to reach it. I would know if you were eating or drinking something – in your case, probably canapés and a glass of champagne (whenever you noticed this in me, it would be a cup of tea and a biscuit). I would know if you had a cold.

Insofar as I could do it, you taught it to me, this ability to pay attention; though to be honest I never properly understood what you were trying to say. You learned the trick of it so early! Michael told me he asked you to marry him because he had never met anyone before who was so *present.* I didn't know what he meant, then. I do now. Is it too late, Maggie? Too late to learn your childhood lesson?

It has shaped your life, and the lack of it has shaped mine.

I used to think our friendship was like a necklace we made together; each bead a shared moment: big and complex – shot through with swirling colours, exciting, bold – or little and dull, depending on circumstances.

And when we parted after meeting up for lunch or a drink, or put the phone down at the end of a call, the necklace would go back into the velvet box, until next time.

I sit at the desk in what is laughingly called our study, and I think of you. I haven't done that for years, but this morning I was digging around in a cupboard for a pair of sandals – it's hot today – and I found a different sort of box that piercingly reminded me of you. So I've got it here, on the table beside me.

I'm sixty; as are you, of course. I haven't seen a recent photo of you, but my guess is that I look it, and you don't. My hair's gone grey and is no-nonsense short; my clothes are 'comfortable', mostly second-hand, and old; and we still live in the shabby little Victorian semi which Alan and I bought when we were married, soon after we graduated.

You, on the other hand, still look much as you did when we were twenty – at least, you did in that last photo you sent – only, these days, tanned and elegant: one of those women who grow more beautiful with the years, not less. And you and Michael live in a luminous white house in Sydney overlooking the harbour, and nothing could be more different from the photographs I've seen of it than what I can see now from my battered swivel chair.

The furniture in our study's awful: the tatty sofa was thrown out by a friend and clashes with the armchair which Alan's brother found on a skip; that's where our desk belongs, its cheap self-assembly panels never having been designed to withstand the years of heavy use to which they've been subjected – the supports parted company from the frames long ago, and the drawers don't slide along runners any more and fall into each other. The room itself is as bad: the walls are still covered in that woodchip paper I so hated and which we've somehow never found the energy to strip off; it badly needs repainting, as does the frame of the window that looks out onto our neglected back garden. Neither of us is a gardener but I think either of us could easily have learned to make a lovely garden, if we'd had the heart.

I sit, holding that necklace in my hands as it were, and thinking about the 'now' that each bead represents. I always thought that 'now' was a word that described my activity of this moment – whatever I'm currently doing – but your understanding was different.

I haven't taken the necklace out of the velvet box for years. I run the beads through my fingers and I go back to the beginning, when everything was clear, before things went wrong between us.

Oh Maggie, I remember you!

I remember that photo of us when we were three, in a paddling-pool in your garden on some hot summer day, wearing nothing but our panties and (doubtless) layers of sun cream (especially you, with your red curls and fair freckled skin); you sitting on the edge, laughing, as all the water poured out around you, and me looking anxious, because the water's meant to be *in* the pool. Typical of us both, that: I was a tidy child and liked things to be in their place. You wanted to have fun and to make things happen.

That memory's a big, joyful bead – blue and red and gold – the very first one.

And I remember, when we were eight, that first time you took my hand and launched us down the middle of your steep road on our new roller-skates, letting go half way down so we could each veer over to opposite lamp-posts at the bottom and grab them and spin round, which stopped us hurtling across the T-junction into whatever unsuspecting traffic might innocently be driving along. Good thing roads were less busy then; and good thing our mums never knew! Especially, on the many occasions afterwards, good thing they never knew how close we came to missing the lamp-posts; or about the two instances when we each actually did, escaping collision by not much and sheepishly having to explain ourselves to a very frightened driver.

That's a whole series of little beads in a variety of shapes and colours: bright, scary, and triumphant.

Oh Maggie, I remember the razzle-dazzle of you at school, always laughing, surrounded by eager groups of hangers-on; effortlessly good at everything (while I was 'good at art', but not much else); charming the teachers who'd set out to tell you off and then delivering clever, quirky pieces of work over which they shook their heads and smiled: original, inventive, playful.

Odd, I thought as we grew older, that we should be friends. But there was a real bond. And when something came up that required a deeper understanding of character than usual, you used to say to people, 'Oh, I don't know, ask Kate. She sees those things.'

And it was true, I often did. At least, I could spot distress. I knew when our fierce French teacher Mam'zelle Jacques suffered weeks of agonising eye pain, although she never told us; when our history teacher Mr Dobson's son was dying of cancer; and when Lindsay Baker in our class was going through the break-up of her first love affair and didn't want anyone to know. I was a good pain-monitor. It was an uncomfortable sort of gift, but it gave me status: a place in your world.

I love the schoolgirl beads: at this distance they're rounded, even, and untroubled.

And sometimes I could foresee consequences that weren't clear to you. Like that time you and Roz bet that you could go to morning registration, take the bus to Brighton, go skinny-dipping off the nudist beach, call in at a bar and be back in time for afternoon registration, without anyone noticing. You'd have the bus tickets, bar receipt and a photo as evidence, you'd make a mint, you said. And it would be such *fun*!

But I knew that however dozy some of the staff might be, you weren't going to get past Miss Franklin's Jane Austen class, second period; she wasn't one to miss you. And it just felt all wrong. I knew it wouldn't end well and that it wouldn't have been worth it, and you listened, remember? So when Miss Franklin looked up and said, straight off, 'Where's Roz? And Julie, and Frances?', you were there to shoot me a quick look and keep your head down.

Someone spiked Roz's drink at the bar that day; she was so ill that the other two had to phone home and get help, which meant that they not only missed the bus home and afternoon registration, but also, as punishment, the sixth form ball the following Saturday.

We'd all been looking forward to our first ball, but for you it was more than just fun, it was a revelation: something in you was born that night. I watched you walk stiffly through to the ballroom in your gorgeous new gown which, half an hour previously, you'd felt all awkward wearing, not knowing how to stand, or what to do with your hands. You stopped in the doorway; quite still, you slowly took in the sparkly chandeliers, the orchestra in their dinner jackets playing, the shiny empty floor stretching before you and the clusters of shy girls and lads in their unaccustomed finery, self-consciously gathered in corners.

Then you set your shoulders, lifted your chin, and half-danced into that room, lightly, on the balls of your feet, and made it yours. It was as if all your life had been a preparation for that moment: a fish released into the sea; a falcon with its jesses cut.

No one would have believed, seeing you dance that night, that your only experience of the waltz till then had been Miss Thomas's stultifying class. The wonder was not that you knew the steps so surprisingly well, although that *was* surprising; what took our breath away was the rush of fluid joy and natural grace in which everything suddenly came together in you: the way you held your arms, your head; the way you moved so that your dress swung and floated around you - anyone would have thought you'd been dancing all your life.

As the evening wore on, people stopped stumbling about to watch you. You ended up dancing with one of the dancing masters at the boys' school, remember? An impromptu display of just the two of you, down the length of the room, while the rest of us stood in a big oval around the edge and watched. Dance after glorious dance, until the 'carriages' were called.

When he bowed low and kissed your hand in goodbye, and we applauded, we all knew we had seen something remarkable.

I remember your grateful hug a little later, as we waited to go home. You said, 'Oh, Kate! You hold me *steady*.'

That bead's so precious to me! Clear as glass, the colour of champagne.

I didn't know it then, but it marked the moment before everything changed.

Well, it would, wouldn't it? The end of our schooldays – the beginning of everything else.

I was desperate to get into art school, into the Slade, and was spending endless hours preparing my portfolio and agonising over how fierce the competition was; but I imagined – we all did – that competition wasn't something that would bother *you*. You'd sail into whatever you wanted, as you always had. You were especially good at languages by then – French, Spanish, Italian. It was just a question of what it would be: Oxford, Cambridge?

'No,' you'd said. 'I've had enough of school. I want to travel, have some fun.'

'Will you do VSO then?' When we were young that was a common aspiration; 'gap years' were unusual at that time.

'No,' you'd said again. 'I think I'll be an air stewardess.'

'What?' I'd been shocked, and I remember your eyes had narrowed.

'And what's *wrong* with being an air stewardess?'

'Nothing, Maggs.' I'd tried to recover myself. 'It's just that – well, anyone can do that, but you could do *anything*.'

'If I can do *anything*,' you'd said with exaggerated emphasis, 'then I can do that, can't I? It'll be fun. I can always do something else later, if I want to.'

That being undeniably true, even your parents had shrugged; and you'd got your way, as usual.

A little polka dot bead, that: all the colours of the rainbow.

I did make the Slade – oh, I was proud! And that began a new series of beads, didn't it: the ones of our first long-distance phone calls, when I was at college and you were somewhere far away with BOAC – Delhi, Bangkok, New York: our first year after school. I'd get a call out of the blue at all kinds of funny times of day or night, partly because you weren't good at calculating time differences, but also because you knew I wouldn't mind. I loved to hear your voice.

We were so far apart, suddenly; and doing such different things.

I've never been as happy as I was at the Slade. I'd go to a lecture, and a new universe would open before me with a dozen paths to follow; I'd go to a seminar, and something familiar would present itself to me in a way I'd never seen before. But the best, the most miraculous thing was discovering what you were pleased to call my 'genius'. I laughed to hear you, but the joy of discovery was so thrilling that I didn't have a better word for it than yours. To discover painting: to learn how to look: to learn colour and form and light: nothing, nothing before or since has ever come close to it.

And for that reason I didn't understand *you*. What were you doing, messing about with something which anyone could do, wasting your gifts and your time? Why didn't you come home and study?

That's the nub of it, dear Maggie, isn't it? *That's* where we began to part company, though I never knew it at the time.

You said, 'There are so many expectations at home – parents, teachers, exam results – all that. But what about me, what do *I* want? I don't know who I am or what I want to do, Kate. All my life so far I've just done what someone else said to do. But now it's up to me, right? And I don't know! So I've taken myself away, out of everything that's familiar, to be by myself, to travel, to get to know myself. I'm not like you.'

'No, I know – '

'I mean, I don't have your talent.'

'*What?*' I remember being stunned. 'You have more talent than anyone I know!'

'Not that I can point to, not like yours,' you'd said. 'In your case, it's dead easy – you have to paint. It would be a crime if you didn't. But I *could* do lots of things – apparently. So what, out of all the possibles, *shall* I do? What do I *want?*'

'Why don't you just choose something and try it out, see how it goes?'

'Because I'm scared I'd just be sucked into it, it would be good enough, you know? Whereas what I really want is to find the one thing that jolts my heart, that takes my breath away, that I want to give my life to.'

'Maggs, I really don't get this. I mean fine, find that! But how is being an air stewardess helping?'

'I'm not sure.'

'There you are then!' I pounced on the uncertainty in your voice. 'So come home, Maggs!'

'I mean, I can't explain it, just like that, in a sentence.'

'Try me.'

'Okay.' I remember, you took a deep breath. 'My head is full of Austen, Dante, factory acts – a ton of stuff I reproduced as required, the "A"s were good, so great. They're the finish of my childhood, if you know what I mean – all the past things. And then there's the future – the rest of my life. And in between, there's now. I want to stop for a bit right there and think about that "now", about how to join up the past things and the future ones the best way I can.'

'Yes, and? The air stewardess thing?'

'It's like a clean piece of paper. If I'm not studying I want to work, obviously – not just hang around. So I thought to myself okay, what work can I do, that will help me work things out?'

'And?'

'And for a start I want to be somewhere else, right away from home and everything I know, so I can have a clean sheet. Well, this job really gives me that! I get the chance to see more of the world than I could any other way, *and* get paid for it.'

'Uh-huh, I see that.'

'And actually I love the travel, and I don't mind the work – it's easy – quite fun too. Most of the crews are good company, and quite often you get passengers who are really interesting.'

'And that's enough?' I was amazed.

'Well actually no, the other part is what's hard to describe to someone else.'

'Maggs, it's me you're talking to.'

'I know! Well, are you feeling patient? I'm working it out.'

'Go on.'

'This "now" stuff. I've been reading books, thinking.'

'Uh-huh?'

'Mm. You know how you can't affect the past, it's already gone?'

'Yes – '

'And you can't be in the future, it's not here yet?'

'Mm-hm.'

'So, the only place you can actually live, is right now. This moment. And *that's* how you affect your future.'

'Well, of course.' I was puzzled. 'So?'

'So you need to know who you are and what you want, otherwise you won't know what things to do now, and you'll end up doing whatever comes to hand. And if you don't have direction, you can't make the most of what you're doing now anyhow – you'll be thinking say about what happened yesterday or what you have to do tomorrow, you won't be paying attention, you'll just get through it on the way to the next thing.'

'But Maggs, that's normal – '

'Yes, unfortunately! But you can change that. Kate, suppose you sat in the chair where you are now, talking to me, and really thought about it. When we've hung up, stay there. Be still; be aware of your body, how it feels – feet, legs, arms; breathe, and be aware of your breathing. Let your eyes stray around the room and take in what you see. Is the window open?'

'Yes, it's a lovely day – '

'Good, then what can you hear, what can you smell? What can you see out of the window? *Inhabit* this moment, Kate, it's yours, where you are. You're nowhere else in all place or time, only here. The past is gone and the future isn't here yet – you can't live in either of them. But now – *now* is where you actually are. Always. It's the only place where you can act. So, really notice everything you can about it, especially what you like in it, what feeds you. It will help you decide what you most want to do, right now. Do this often, and you'll start getting a really good picture of who you are in the world, what you want to do in it. You'll not just mindlessly go through things with your mind elsewhere, not having noticed what's under your nose. Which is what people mostly do.'

'Maggs, I'm really happy. I like what I'm doing, I don't need to keep stopping to think about it. And anyway, I don't have the time to do this stopping and – and mooching about stuff, I'm busy.'

'Oh Kate, it doesn't take a lot of time. It really doesn't. Try it, you'll see what I mean. It makes you aware. Of yourself, and of other people, and what's going on around you. It makes you love life so much.'

'I'm already perfectly aware, Maggs, and I already love life.'

That bead's a strange one: so bubbly and clear and bright on one side, but as I look now, sort of grim and gathering-dark on the other.

Oh Maggie, I wonder what would have happened if I'd listened to you?

I left college and married Alan. When we bought our house it was cheap because it needed most things doing to it. Alan had just joined the family firm, who were builders, and I settled down to work for them too, as they were going through a rough patch just then and couldn't afford to employ someone properly. I hung my final-year work on the walls of our little house and thought I could always go back to painting later.

Alan was steady and knowledgeable. I liked how he'd turn his hand to anything, how he was willing and generous, and calming to have around. He was gentle, kind.

He still is.

But he's no businessman, and his brothers aren't either; so after their father died, there was simply one rough patch after another.

Meanwhile, on a trip to Australia, you met Michael. He was tall, dark and handsome, just like in the stories; an investment banking associate with a global financial services firm, and ten years older than us: experienced, clever, witty, courteous. The only time I met him I felt very grown-up; he had the gift of making other people sparkle.

The Michael-beads are balls of multicoloured excitement and delight. I remember the wonderful dinner at the Savoy when you introduced us to him – it was like having dinner with film stars. As we followed the Maître d' to our table, people stopped talking as we went past to stare at you both: he so handsome, you so beautiful, both of you tall and slim and elegant – the most striking couple I ever saw.

I remember that as we went back to our little house on the train late that night, Alan and I, I knew for sure that fairy tales really do happen. Happy ever after, just like that.

And that evening marked the beginning of a second run of long-distance calls, this time mostly from Sydney where you settled after you got married. Big, clear, happy beads, these: marking the births of your twins Toby and Tamara, and, two years later, of Natalie; of reams of photographs showing your lovely house, the five of you on holiday in several dozen gorgeous places, snaps of everyone at home, fooling about.

And out of that happiness, Maggie, there grew your interest in charity work – or, as you used to say, 'getting involved in the world around me'. Firstly it was the plight of the aborigines, a people you grew to love and honour and whose case you took to the Australian government, with considerable success: I saw you on the news once.

And after that, there was the water charity in Africa, and street children in Brazil. And now, who knows?

But it wasn't like that with us.

Alan and I have lurched from one crisis to another. We never had the money to do up our house, or travel, or indeed do anything other than survive whatever the current difficulty was, and try to make ends meet.

We decided we couldn't afford children. Over the years I became accustomed, little by little, to smaller and smaller horizons. I learned to make do. We are English, after all; you can't have everything.

'Kate, I'm worried about you.'

'Don't be, we're fine.'

'But you're not painting, are you?'

'Well no, not just at the mo – '

'What was the last thing you painted?'

'I can't quite remember.'

'Oh Kate! *How* long have you been married?'

'Um – eight years.'

'Exactly! What are you doing right now?'

'Talking to you – '

'You know what I mean!'

I didn't answer, and you said, 'Remember the sixth form dance, Kate?'

'How could I forget, you were the belle of the ball – '

'Yes, and if you hadn't talked sense into me I wouldn't have been able to go, and it's fair to say my life would have been quite different. I owe you tons, Kate.'

'Don't be daft, I had nothing to do with your triumph that night.'

'You certainly did! I learned joy that night. I discovered how you *do* it, how you transform what you know, fuse it all together. But I had to take hold of it – take a risk, you know? And that gave me the courage to go for it; not to put up with anything less than what I really wanted.'

'I remember. I watched you as you stood in the doorway, before you stepped out onto the dance floor.'

'So dear Kate, I listened to you beforehand and took your advice, and golly, you were right. So please, will you listen to me now? It's every bit as important!'

'I'll listen, Maggie, but I'm not sure what you mean.'

'What are you doing right now?'

'The firm's accounts.'

'Good at maths, are you, all of a sudden?'

'No, you know I'm terrible! But there's no one else to do it, and we can't afford to take anybody on.'

'Kate, please listen to me, it matters so much.' I could hear the distress in your voice. 'You're a painter. Not just any old painter, either – it was always obvious you have real genius.'

'You used to say that, you were sweet.'

'No I wasn't, "sweet" is not a word that applies to me! At school, who got the best "A" level Art A in the school's history?'

'Yes, I know, but – '

'But nothing! Who was the most talented pupil she'd ever had, according to old Paint-by-Numbers?'

'Well, she did pretty much paint by numbers, what would she know?'

'She still got you the best A the school's ever had, must've done something right! Kate, your paintings were *brilliant,* you know they were! What about that self-portrait, the one where the lower school all followed you around calling you Rembrandt after it was hung in the hall? And what about – '

'Maybe, Maggs, but now is different – '

'I can see that, and it's a tragedy, Kate. You *must* paint, it's quite obviously what you were born to do. You must arrange your life so you can get back to it.'

'You don't understand, Maggs, I can't. Maybe later, when things are on a more solid footing. But not now. It wouldn't be fair.'

'Fair on whom? It doesn't sound to me as if Alan's doing what he was made for, either. Is *he* happy?'

'Well, no.'

'How does he usually feel, would you say?'

'Um - anxious and afraid.'

'So how about looking at the whole thing together? Suppose you both gave real thought to who you are and what you want in your lives – you each only have the one!'

'Oh Maggie, it's all very well for you, you don't have the difficulties we have, you don't know what it's like.'

'That's true, Kate, I don't. But that's largely because I work at what I know suits me, and where I'm confident I can do something useful. It strikes me both you and Alan are using the wrong tools for the wrong job, and you really don't need to. Life is huge, Kate. There are many alternatives. How can you know what would happen if you stepped out into something completely different, that *suited* you – unless you give it a go?'

Oh Maggie, you tried. You really did. You only gave up when I wouldn't talk to you any more. I remember your last sad comment: 'Oh Kate! And you who used to see so clearly!'

My paints lie undisturbed in the boxes I placed them in when I left college. They were a luxury, after all; for one day, far in the future, when there might be the time for me to 'mess about with them', as Alan says.

I look back over all the beads. Especially the later ones – so dismal and clouded and sad.

And each of those crises that we battled through, Alan and I, seemed so huge at the time! But now, as I look back over the pinched and sorry years, it looks like an endless desert of nothing: level, flat.

Dear Maggie. I wonder if it's too late, after all this time, to claim my place in your transforming, growing life; the one in which a meeting, a conversation, is dynamic, and *changes* us.

I lay down my imaginary necklace and open the very physical box that's been beside me all morning, and lift out a battered pair of child's roller-skates. As I weigh them in my hand – so heavy! The kind you used to buckle onto your shoes, proper metal, leather straps – I wonder if you'll remember taking my hand and launching me down your steep road all those years ago, the first time I wore these, when they were new.

I put them down on the floor, gently.

Then I lean across the table, lift the phone out of its socket, dial your number, and press 'call.'

7. Buttercups

LOVE THE EARTH

'The earth is the Lord's, and everything in it,
the world, and all who live in it;
for he founded it upon the seas and
established it upon the waters.'
Psalm 24:1-2

It had rained overnight, and the scruffy grass that edged the pavement was unusually lustrous. It smelt like heaven to Scraps, who, tail up and nose down, joyfully tracked in it several traces of neighbourhood dogs, noting as he went the presence of cats, foxes and squirrels, fresh earth, various weeds, car exhausts, the succession of new coffee shops serving the new city community down to the Indian take-away on the corner, the dozen perfumes and aftershaves of passing pedestrians, the combination of old clothes, shoes, sweat and beer of his owner Stanley trailing reluctantly behind, and the reassuring aroma of his own urine. All that, and a thousand other fragrances tantalisingly floated to him on the breeze.

Scraps was the gift of a rag-bag ancestry. There was a dash of spaniel about his long, silky ears which gave him a deceptively soft expression, but his bright eyes and jaunty gait were all terrier, and the rest – well, it was anyone's guess. He had rough, short, brown hair with some white (except for the ears which were glossy chocolate), was smallish and stocky, and unfailingly cheerful.

This was just as well, since Stanley was predominantly gloomy. Stanley was a disappointed man; he hadn't expected much from life and he'd been proved right.

Born in Acton a few years before the war to a single mother and never having known his father, he'd been evacuated with his older sister Mavis when he was eight and she was ten; and owing to a mix-up at the reception area they'd been separated and had gone to different families, which hadn't helped. A few months later their mother back in London had died of pneumonia. Those two events had shaped the rest of Stanley's life.

He didn't remember much from before the war. Oddly the only clear memory he had of his mother was of sitting on a patch of grass with her while she held a buttercup under his chin and asked, 'Here, our Stan, do you like butter?' It was a hot day and his mother was laughing. She was wearing a blue polka dot dress and an apron with flowers on it.

For the rest of his life he could shut his eyes and feel the tickle of the buttercup against his skin and the sun on his back. It was perhaps his last memory of feeling warm and safe.

Stanley was billeted on a farmer and his wife, Mr and Mrs Baxter, deep in the Kentish countryside. Mr Baxter, who had a dozen Jersey cows and sixty-odd sheep, ran the farm single-handed with the assistance of neighbouring farmers when needed, and was glad to have unpaid help on the premises. He was a dour man who disliked company and who would do without the neighbours' help if he possibly could. Mrs Baxter, a downtrodden, unhappy woman who resented the relentless nature of farm work, felt lonely during the long days, stuck out in the middle of nowhere. Their fifteenth-century farmhouse was damp and cold.

Stanley earned his keep and loathed every second of it.

He was frightened of the big cows he had to shift from field to barn and back again, and so terrified of their huge proximity when Mr Baxter tried to teach him milking that the farmer gave up in disgust.

Lambing was the worst, though. For years afterwards the unexpected sight of a field of lambs – from a train window, say – made him feel sick and faint. Night after night he'd been hauled out of bed in the early watches of a raw morning to stand in the whipping sleet and bitter cold, often for hours, before being scraped out of sodden or frost-crackling inadequate clothing, bundled into his uniform and sent to unfamiliar, difficult school with a piece of cold toast in his pocket for breakfast.

During lambing-time he was always too tired to understand or explain, too cold to concentrate, and too defeated to care.

It was hard to know which had been worse: having to stand quite still holding a large torch steady (which in snow could mean literally being frozen into position), or being forced to be the second pair of hands helping the sheep thrust their lambs into the world. He was frightened by what seemed to him the poor ewes' pain and he never got used to the messy, difficult process. He was haunted still by the occasional poor little stillborn mites, terrified that something he'd done might have killed each one.

It seemed to him that nature was haphazard, cruel and inexplicable. He hated it. Even hot summer days were no relief: he would either be stuck in a stuffy classroom or sent to work in a neighbour's field to help get in the harvest, where he'd be bitten or stung by things or burned by the sun. And the animals didn't help; in his experience, they mostly hurt you or died.

It was a horrible world.

He thought that as soon as he possibly could he would go back to London, where he could live instead with things men made: roads, bridges, buildings. A predictable world: a world of dependable, inanimate things which you could control.

And meanwhile he retreated deep into himself. He learned to be careful and self-reliant. Whom else could he trust?

After the war Stanley did indeed return to London, where he lived with a distant aunt until he was old enough to leave school. Mavis joined him there; she'd had a quiet war with a family who had two children much younger than she was, and came back ready, as she said, 'to be normal again'. Stanley didn't say much about the farm. He was more grateful than he knew how to express to be again among streets and pavements and concrete and stone, and swore he would never leave London again.

Nor did he. The war had left London with almost 80,000 buildings wrecked beyond repair and all but a third of the City virtually destroyed; a lad interested in learning the building trade had only to look about him. As soon as he could, Stanley left school and got himself apprenticed. He discovered an interest in realising other people's designs: creating solutions to the technical problems thrown up by the projects his employers took on. When, in due course, he became involved in the regeneration of London's docklands, he stayed there for the rest of his working life.

During all those years he kept himself to himself. He preferred it that way; nothing happened to change his view that the world around him was broken and unstable, including – perhaps especially – the people in it. People were responsible for wars, famine, pollution.

He wanted nothing to do with any of them. He withdrew; and, so gradually that he never noticed it, he simply closed down. If no one could reach him, no one could hurt him, either.

The exception to this was Mavis, whom he saw from time to time and always at Mavis's instigation. 'Being normal' for her was working in the personnel department of one of the big banks in the City. She liked Victorian fiction, enjoyed work 'do's' where she was sociable and chatty as long as nobody came too close, and kept a dog. She worried that her brother never did anything but work and never 'got out', and she felt responsible – who else was there? So she made sure they met for a drink occasionally, or had a sandwich lunch in a pub.

One of the first docklands projects on which Stanley worked was an elegant warehouse redevelopment into flats, and he thought he might buy one for himself; somewhat as an afterthought he suggested that Mavis do the same. It was a good investment, he said; but to be honest what most attracted him about it was that it was new. There was nothing there.

Mavis thought it was a good idea too, for entirely different reasons. It wasn't far from her work, and she'd been thinking for some time that maybe she should be keeping a closer eye on Stanley. Her mother would have liked it.

And since neither of them had married, it was easy enough.

So they'd chosen two adjacent ground-floor flats at Mavis's insistence, because she wanted access for her dog to what were then laughingly called the 'communal gardens'. She was also a bit of a bibliophile and had collected quite a number of those Victorian novels, with some Agatha Christie and P D James thrown in – 'and I can't be climbing up and down stairs with them all the time.' Stanley had said 'don't be daft, there are lifts, we're not in the dark ages,' and she'd said 'but still,' so that was that.

And it had worked well, surprisingly. One dog had succeeded another for Mavis, and the communal gardens, once landscaped and given time, had indeed become worth having – not that Stanley noticed them. If ever he felt a whisper of dissatisfaction with his life, he quelled it and simply worked longer hours, gaining a reputation for being hardworking and punctilious which served him well; and when he came home he relaxed in front of the telly or (occasionally) read a book. That way there weren't any nasty surprises, and his days passed easily enough. It was a pattern he kept into retirement, during which he still did the odd job, to keep his hand in. And if his world shrivelled over the years until there was virtually nothing in it but himself, that suited him fine: a man had a responsibility to take care of himself. He was all right.

He reasoned that people were outgrowing the natural world they'd come from, and put his dissatisfaction with it down to the fact that scientific advances were making it obsolete. The growing fashion for 'natural' preferences infuriated him.

'It's stupid,' he said to Mavis, 'we can genetically modify our food to give us three, four times the yield – feed the hungry, all that. Why would you want to do it the "natural" way, and be so much less efficient?'

'You don't know anything about it,' said Mavis. 'Get your facts straight before you start sounding off.'

'I know all I need to know!' said Stanley. 'There was this bloke on the telly – '

'There always is,' said Mavis, 'especially in your case, but what about real life? It's like I keep saying – you need to get out more. Meet people! Look around you! You used to spend all the time you weren't working in front of the B telly, and now you've retired you go on doing odd jobs and still spend all the rest of your time in front of the B telly – '

'I do not!' said Stanley, 'I go down the pub a lot.'

'Yes, and sit in a corner with your pint and watch the snooker and not speak to a living soul. I've seen you.'

'Well, I don't like people,' said Stanley with relish, knowing that would get her going. 'Don't trust 'em. We'll have good enough artificial intelligence soon to design whatever sort of people we want, and then you won't get all the wars and crime, and people being plain daft. Robots, that's what we need. We're not far off. And *then,*' said Stanley, warming to his favourite theme, '*then* we can all go populate other planets because by then we'll have the technology, and this sorry bit of stone and muck can sink back into the black hole where it came from.'

Mavis knew when it was time to move on. 'Talk about people being plain daft, you should hear yourself, you silly B,' she'd say, and go out to make a cup of tea to restore her temper.

She had popped in to see Stanley every day after they'd moved into the flats, and Stanley hadn't realised how central a part of his life Mavis had become until she'd died suddenly of a stroke, on a chilly November day some six months previously.

There had been a letter with the will. 'Stanley, if you're reading this it's because I've gone off to join Mother. Hope you're all right. Basically it all goes to you and you can do whatever you want with any of it, but you've got to take on Scraps. Do you hear? Otherwise it all goes to the local dogs' home. I mean it, Stan. It's all in proper language in the will. I want you to have him. He'll do you good, get you out. You need to join the human race, you daft old b – .'

Stanley had stared at the words, recognising for the first time the provenance of his sister's curious habitual expletive. Of course: those genteel Victorian stories in which rude words were not spelled out. He felt a stab of regret that he had never made the connection, never said to her, 'You silly woman! Say the *word*, it's me you're talking to, not some bishop!' And then he realised it was a little late to be claiming intimacy – he who had always resisted it.

So he had 'taken on' Scraps as requested, slapping Mavis's sheet of instructions on his fridge door with the fridge magnet that said '*I'm* all right, it's the others,' and settled down to sharing his life with another creature for the first time.

It wasn't plain sailing. He wasn't used to considering anyone's needs other than his own, and got frustrated. He soon discovered, for example, that the communal gardens, useful though they were, had to be supplemented by a daily walk or Scraps became intolerable (the instructions were unfortunately quite correct on that point). So Stanley sulkily factored it in, feeling put-upon.

The best he could do was walk Scraps to the pub. That way at least there was some point to it.

So that was how Scraps and Stanley happened to be making their way towards Stanley's favourite watering-hole one sunny May morning. Scraps was usually good – having worked out the route within the first few days – and trotted along obediently enough, so Stanley kept the lead in his pocket; but today was different. One minute he was pottering along ahead as usual, and the next he'd shot down a side street and vanished.

Stanley swore. He knew the area pretty well, and those parts in which he'd put up buildings like the back of his hand, but this wasn't one of those. The pub he favoured was in a rough, unconverted neighbourhood and he went to it because he'd always gone there; when he'd first moved in, it had been the nearest: a fair-sized Victorian pub on a corner, you couldn't miss it.

The trouble was he didn't know the streets around it, never having had occasion to go into them. And now he wondered why – as he turned into the side street down which Scraps had disappeared – this area hadn't been demolished long ago as had so many others, to make way for new buildings like the ones he'd worked on.

The narrow terraced houses were neglected and run down. Many had doors and windows boarded up, and there was graffiti on the walls and rubbish in the gutters. Stanley wrinkled his nose in disgust. Why would people live like this? It confirmed him in all his worst prejudices.

The street ended in a rough piece of waste ground which had clearly been used as a rubbish tip over a long period of time. He surveyed it with distaste. There were heaps of junk – old prams, tyres, bikes, washing machines, assorted piles of plasterboard, rotting timber, bricks, chests of drawers with drawers missing – name it and some sorry remnant was sure to be there.

But as he looked more closely, choosing where to step, he realised that the rubbish was arranged in an attempt at orderly piles according to type: someone had apparently sorted it preparatory to disposing of it, and localised efforts had been made to clear the ground.

He gingerly skirted a small mountain of old tyres and the land opened out before him, cleared of rubbish but choked with the usual wasteland crops of nettles, old roots and wild grass. And at this end, energetically digging up brambles by pushing home a large garden fork with a booted foot, bending over and then scooping the fork up again in a practised movement, was a pencil-thin young woman.

She had straight, bright pink hair that had been cut short on one side and long on the other some time ago, so for a moment he thought he was looking at a strange hat; then he realised that what he'd taken to be the hat's black centre was in fact the good few inches of her real hair colour, and realised he wasn't. She had on tight faded jeans and a yellow strappy top, and had tied a light jacket around her waist by its sleeves which had the word 'BRIDGET' in big letters along the back. She looked up as he came closer. She had a stud above her right nostril, three rings in her lower lip and a row of little rings all along the edge of her left ear. She looked about twenty.

'Hi,' she said. 'Great! You come to help?'

'No,' said Stanley. 'I hate messing about in the muck.'

She leant on the handle of her fork. 'Why?'

Stanley stared at her. 'It's dirty and it's pointless and even if you *had* to do it a machine would do it better in half the time, so why bother? And anyway, what's it to you?'

The girl stared back. 'Cheerful old bugger, aren't you?' she said, conversationally. 'If you're not here to help, what did you come down here for?'

'My dog – I'm looking for my dog.'

She pointed. 'He's down there – he'll be fine, it's all fenced off, he can't get out.' She grinned at him. 'Nice little dog. You can't be all bad then, eh! Not if you have a nice little dog like him.'

'He was my sister's dog. She died.'

'Oh. That explains it, then.' She went back to her digging,

leaving Stanley speechless. He was mostly angry at himself – what in blazes had made him tell her that?

Unfazed, she went on, 'Since you're here, how about giving me a hand anyway? There's a ton to do.'

'Why don't you get a council grant, government money?'

'We did – a little anyway, not much.' She squinted round at him. 'This is a council project, it's council land. Only there's not much money. So we got to do most of the clearing ourselves.' She went back to her work.

'Well, hire a digger then. Do it properly.' Stanley was glad to get a little of his own back. 'And anyway, you'll be here for ever if you don't.'

'Not if other people help. And there's quite a few of us. And we can't afford a digger.' She spoke in small bursts, between digs of the fork.

Despite himself, he watched her for a couple of minutes, noticing suddenly that there was a small child sitting in the grass some ten feet away, engrossed in a circle of dolls and plastic teacups. Presumably she belonged to the young woman; she had her black hair, which was just about all he could see of her as she bent over her toys. He hadn't thought the young woman old enough to have a child, but then he didn't know much about that kind of thing. The child was small – three, perhaps? She was quite silent, he noted approvingly. It made him look slightly more favourably upon the young woman. What on earth was she doing? Eventually curiosity got the better of him.

'What's wrong with that stuff, why are you digging it up?'

'Nothing. I'm making a butterfly transect.' She looked round, and seeing his blank expression, said, 'Butterflies like flying in lines, so if you make them little corridors, it's easier for 'em to get to the bramble flowers on both sides, plus you can walk the path and report on 'em, see? The butterfly bloke who's advising us is down there – ' she gestured – 'which is why I can be digging, we're not meant to be here by ourselves.' She grinned. 'Great old bloke. Knows all kinds of stuff – was showing us bee orchids earlier, and ragwort, and he reckons in the winter we can have goldfinches feeding on the seeds of those teasels over there.'

'Oh.' Stanley took that in. 'Was it you sorted out the rubbish back there, into piles?'

'Me and some others, yeah. It's going to be great.'

Stanley thought he'd misheard. 'Pardon?'

'It's going to be great.' She bent to lay the fork down carefully, and straightened up again. 'See this?' She swept her arm across the extent of the tussocky, abandoned land. 'Community project, this is. When it's cleared this'll be a park, and down there will be allotments, for anybody – no waiting-lists, just yours if you want it, to plant stuff. Up here will be swings and slides for the kids, tables and benches for the mums, maybe even a caf! See that dip, down there?' She pointed. 'That'll be a pond. We'll have tadpoles, ducks.' She turned to him, her eyes shining. 'It'll be *brilliant!*'

Stanley was nonplussed. He had no idea how to respond to her enthusiasm, and after an awkward moment said lamely the only thing that came into his head.

'Why?'

'*Why?*' she repeated incredulously, staring at him in her turn. 'Have you seen this *street?* We *live* here. This – dump – ' she gestured all around – 'is where our kids play. Like my Em here, see?' She indicated the little girl. 'They don't have anywhere else.'

'Why don't you get the council to build you a playground or something?'

'Because first off they won't, they don't have money for that. But also, that's not what we want.'

'What do you want, then?'

She looked at him curiously. 'We want land that's ours, that we can grow stuff on. We want the kids to know beans and carrots come out of the earth, not out of the supermarket. We want to put a seed in, and see it come up a sunflower. We want to play with them on grass that's clean and nice and full of daisies and not in the street that's all dirty. And us mums – we want somewhere where we can do good things like that, and sit around and chat, and – and just be together.'

'Well, the kids could play and the mums could chat if you had one of those big indoor play areas. Much more practical. Why don't you make an application for one of them?'

'You're not listening, are you?' she said. 'The kids *are* indoors, most of the time. We want to get them back out. To connect them back to the world they live in, to the earth.'

'I hate the earth,' said Stanley. 'The sooner we get the technology to move on, start over, the better.'

'And meanwhile, what?' said the young woman, scornfully. 'You can't live in technology that's not here yet, you have to live *now*. And anyway, who's going to make this great technology of the future? The kids who are here now, right?' She gave him a straight look and Stanley, who hadn't thought of this, stood silently without an answer.

The young woman's face softened. 'You remind me of my dad,' she said, 'he was in the war, I reckon it screwed him up. Took him a while to come round to any of this. Just didn't care. Does now, though. Gets down here every Saturday to help. Mum says he's a changed man.'

Stanley looked at her with surprise. 'But you're much too young to have a father who was in the war!'

She smiled at him. 'Yeah, I know. I'm twenty-three. I was born when he was sixty-four. He's lots older than my mum. He was a pilot in the Battle of Britain, he was only seventeen. He never talks about it but I was dead proud when I found out. Shut up the girls at school who called him grandpa.' She turned her back to show him the name across the jacket around her waist. 'See that?' she said. '"Bridget. That's what we'll call her, Bridget", he said when I was born, apparently. Mum and me, we reckon it's some old girlfriend who died in the war, but he's never said.' She grinned. 'We reckon he has lots of secrets.'

'It's an unusual name,' said Stanley. 'Nowadays.'

'Yeah. I never liked it till I discovered some nice things about it. It means power and strength, plus there was a Celtic goddess Brigid who was the goddess of agriculture and healing. I like that. So my partner got the jacket done.'

She knelt down and scooped up a large handful of damp earth, which she pressed into Stanley's cupped hands before he realised what was happening.

'Lucky it's been raining,' she said. 'I did this to dad, but your earth is nicer than his was, so you should be even friendlier.'

She put her muddy hands under his and gave them a little push upwards. 'Now you smell that,' she said. 'Have a feel of it. Everything we have grows out of this – vegetables and cereals and fruit trees and grass for the animals we eat, and the trees and plants that give off the oxygen we breathe. Earth is *magic*. Technology!' She shook her head. 'Technology's nothing without this. We need this first. Don't get me wrong, technology's great and we can use it to help us take care of the earth. But if we don't take care of the earth in the first place, if we don't learn the basics for the technology to work *on*, we won't be needing technology for anything else, 'cos we won't be here.'

She paused to catch her breath. Stanley was staring at her. 'You're a surprising young woman, um – Bridget.'

'Well, we've got to *get it*,' she said, 'we've got to *understand*. The earth isn't separate from us. We're a part of it, just like the trees, or a flower. We can't live without it. Look, your little dog over there – he gets it.'

Stanley looked over to where she was pointing and saw Scraps emerge from a bank of scrubby bushes, zig-zagging through the long grass, wholly intent and absorbed, eagerly following a scent.

The little girl, who had been quietly sitting among the teacups all this time, shifted onto her knees, and in doing so caught sight of a clump of flowers growing nearby. She pounced on it and picked one, holding it up. 'Look, Mum!'

'Oh, that's nice, Em,' said Bridget. 'Ask him.'

'Ask me what?' said Stanley.

'If you like butter, of course,' said Bridget. 'Don't tell me you don't know about that either?'

Em got up and scrambled over to him, the little yellow flower waving in her fist. She looked up at him expectantly and her mum, glancing at him and seeing him standing there rigidly, said, 'Well, go on then, bend down to her!'

Stanley clumsily dropped onto one knee, trying not to spill the earth he was still holding in his hands. It was all too much. He was overwhelmed by an earlier sunlit memory and he couldn't help it – he shut his eyes as he felt the tickle of the buttercup against his chin and heard the light young voice say, 'Hey, man, do you like butter?'

He opened his eyes and smiled at Em, who was looking at him hopefully. 'Yes, I do,' he said. 'I like it very much.'

8. The Echoes of Pain

BE KIND

'Therefore, as God's chosen people, holy and dearly loved,
clothe yourselves with compassion, kindness, humility,
gentleness and patience.'
Colossians 3:12

The heel of Joan's shoe snapped off as she hurried up the stairs of the Underground station. Joan always hurried, despite the fact that she always gave herself plenty of time and was always early everywhere. She would have considered it unprofessional to do otherwise; and in Joan's book, that was simply unacceptable.

For Joan was a punctilious woman.

Her clothes were beautifully cut, expensive and perfectly pressed; she usually wore a slate-grey Jaeger suit with a silk blouse (today's was a shade of green which exactly matched her eyes), silk stockings – she knew the places where you could still get those – and highly-polished, black high-heeled shoes. She said you could always tell a lady by her shoes. According to her definition, there weren't many ladies amongst the women in the busy office where she worked, and she didn't think much of them: lightweight girls, in her view, who didn't take enough care.

Actually they wouldn't have spoken that highly of her, either, although Joan was the sort of woman everyone called upon when anything needed doing either immediately or very well. She was infinitely dependable; but as for the rest, there wasn't much to like or dislike – she was private and quiet and didn't join in. Nobody knew anything about her personal life, not even her age: she could have been anything between forty and sixty. She was tall and bony and had that loose-limbed sort of body which should have been graceful, but there was a pinched fastidiousness about her which spoiled her movements. Nobody she worked with would have bothered to enquire why that was, but if anyone had asked Joan, she probably would have put it down to her feet.

Joan hated her feet. They were ugly feet and she was ashamed of them. The bones were squeezed together and they were disfigured by swollen bunions and callouses. She punished her feet by squeezing them into smart, shiny, high-heeled shoes, which she considered appropriate footwear for the legal profession, of which she was a proud representative. And since she scorned the modern fashion of 'letting go' when at home, she wore them there, too.

So she was particularly irritated today as her feet let her down once again on the stairs up from the tube platform.

'Damn!' Joan said, recovering her balance and picking up the offending heel. She was annoyed to see that part of the shoe itself had come away with it, so there was no possibility of repair. She hobbled up to street level and surveyed the shops opposite.

'Good thing I've got the time!' she thought, annoyance giving way for a moment to satisfaction as she contemplated pointing this out to Margery at the office when she got back. Margery thought her time-keeping excessive, and said so. This was the perfect opportunity of proving Margery wrong, and Joan felt a gleam of pleasurable anticipation. Well, the brief she was delivering was to one of their major clients, so what if she hadn't allowed for emergencies?

As luck would have it, there was a shoe shop just across the road. It looked rather small and was clearly a private concern, but it would do, all the same.

On entering, she saw it was indeed small inside. There was an older man who was serving a customer, and a young man who came up to her enquiringly. Joan had rather hoped she might have been served by the older man – she wasn't too fond of the young, especially of young men – but the older one was obviously busy, so she would have to make do with the other. She sighed. It was inconvenient; but although she had a few minutes, she certainly didn't have all day to wait about.

'How may I help you?' asked the young man, courteously enough.

She gave him the broken shoe. 'I'd like another pair like this, please, in a size seven.'

'Won't you sit down?'

Surprised, she did as she was asked, and the young man knelt at once in front of her. 'Would you mind if I looked at your feet?'

What an extraordinary question! she thought, surprise deepening into indignation.

'That won't be necessary,' she said coldly in a tone of voice which usually carried the last word. 'I only want another pair like this.'

'I know,' he said, and smiled at her. His smile was disarming and utterly unexpected, and despite herself she looked at him fully for the first time. He was fair and slight and spotty – totally unprepossessing, in fact – but he had not responded at all to her cutting tone, and on the contrary was still smiling at her, looking her fully in the eyes. His eyes, she noticed, startled, were deep and warm and just at present crinkled up in the smile, and really it was impossible not to smile back. She felt herself responding, tried not to, failed, and looked away. When she glanced back at him his face was in repose, and he was studying his hands.

He raised his eyes and said, 'I know you'd like another pair like this, but if I might look at your feet I could give you some advice, perhaps – '

Joan was mistress of herself again and cut him off smoothly. 'No – thank you. Just let me have what I asked for.'

'Of course.' The young man got up at once and went off to the back of the shop. After less than the usual wait he returned carrying two long boxes, which he laid down on the floor beside her. Her attention was caught by the fluidity and gentleness of his movements. It struck her that he treated the shoes with reverence. Pull yourself together, she thought, what a silly idea.

He knelt in front of her, then opened the first box, lightly folding one sheet of tissue back on itself, then the other, and finally drawing out a glossy black high-heeled shoe – all but an exact replica of the one she was wearing.

'Yes, that's it,' she said, eagerly.

The young man put the shoe down and put out his hand for her stockinged foot. She lifted it and as his fingers closed around it, she became aware of the oddest circumstance.

He was holding her foot lightly and firmly, but it was the peculiarity of the touch that unnerved her. What was it? It took her some moments to understand that what she was experiencing was simply tenderness. Hot on the heels of that realisation was the knowledge that he was trying very hard not to gain by stealth what she had denied him: he was trying not to examine her foot, even though just the feel of it in his hand was telling him things, which he was trying not to process.

This exquisite courtesy was agony enough; but it was the tenderness which broke her. To her horror, she felt the reluctant tears coming and a sob rising in her throat. Panicking, she pretended to cough to cover the sob and looked away, muttering idiotically, 'You can look at it, if you want to.'

The young man took her foot in both his hands and looked down at it. She kept her eyes shut because she was terrified that if she opened them, the tears would all spill out. He cradled her foot in his hands, turning it very lightly this way and that, and although he neither stroked nor pressed it, she was more aware of his touch than she had ever been of any touch in her life. Astounded, she opened her eyes, groped for her handkerchief, mopped up and then looked back at the young man. His head was bent over her foot.

'You see, I wonder whether – well, whether you were a younger child with lots of older brothers and sisters whose shoes you wore.' He shot her a glance, and taking courage from the naked shock on her face went on, 'and therefore, you know, you didn't choose your own shoes then, so it's hard to do that now, and I expect you always go for the same ones. But – well, I imagine they hurt.'

Joan attempted to recover some dignity. She said in a voice that was only slightly strained, 'But you always have to break in new shoes, don't you?'

He smiled at her again, that cheerful, crinkly smile. 'Actually no, not if they fit you well.' He lifted her foot a little, presenting it to her in his hands as if it weren't her own. 'Look, see how the bones are crushed together here? That's because the shoes you wore as a child were too narrow. And here – these bunions are because of pressure, here and here ... '

He went on to list her foot's many imperfections but she wasn't listening any more. Awash with pain and self-pity, she was remembering the crowded council house, the shoving and bullying, the endless hand-me-downs, the battered, broken shoes. 'But Mum, they hurt!' 'Don't be stupid, girl, they're fine. Just need a bit of breaking in. Think of the little children who don't have any shoes at all, and be grateful!'

The young man in the shoe shop pressed gently on the foot he was holding, to get Joan's attention. Then he laid it gently back down on the floor.

'These black shoes are not made for feet like yours. They are – '

'Oh, I know!' said Joan, bitterly. 'They're for the people with the *nice* feet!'

'I'm so sorry, I didn't mean that at all. I meant they are made for thin, narrow feet, which in fact are usually much weaker than yours.' He smiled at her, very gently. 'You have strong feet with good arches. They would respond well to shoes that suited them. And you are already tall. You don't need the height of the heels.'

'But these are the shoes I always wear, they suit what I do – '

She stopped. Really she didn't know what to say. She realised there was a lack of coherence between her words and the reality she was now experiencing, and she didn't know how to bridge the gap. It was like trying to eat soup with a fork.

The young man picked up the other shoe box and and took off the lid. 'May I show you something I think might help?'

She nodded, and watched as he unfolded the tissue on each side and drew out a very different shoe. It was a deep bottle green; it had a short heel instead of the high ones she was used to; its lines were altogether softer and it had a more rounded toe. It was a beautiful, and somehow a chaste, shoe. Wordlessly he held it out to her.

She gave a sort of shrug. She felt as if all her usual perspectives had collapsed into a straight line, as if there was no height anymore – nothing to take one's bearings from. She held out her foot.

The young man took it and slipped first that one, then the other, into the new green shoes. Then he rocked back onto his heels, looked up at her, and waited.

She had never felt so self-conscious before as she stood to walk in a new pair of shoes. She had never felt so young, or raw, or new.

She had never had so little idea what to feel. She thought: I have never *begun* before.

She walked a few steps, aware that she was carrying herself differently. These shoes felt altogether unfamiliar but she understood that they weren't hurting her. Almost she wasn't sure how to walk. She came back and sat down.

'How do you feel?' asked the young man.

'Different.'

'Do the shoes hurt?'

'No.'

He leaned forward and very lightly touched one of the shoes. 'Every step you take in your life, you take with your feet,' he said. 'It's really important that when you walk, your feet don't hurt. Because if they do, every step you take will raise echoes of pain, won't it?'

'It certainly will.' Joan looked at him. 'It does. What makes you so – so wise?'

The boy grinned, suddenly looking very young. 'Oh, I like feet,' he said simply. 'Feet are really interesting. They are all different, nobody is like anybody else, we all have a different walk. Nobody can walk your walk like you.'

And, this time, she smiled back at him.

'Thank you,' she said.

9. The Bear

BE DEPENDENT

'Then Jesus declared ... "All that the Father gives me will come to me, and whoever comes to me I will never drive away. For I have come down from heaven not to do my will but to do the will of him who sent me."'
John 6:38

Sometimes when I wake, even now, for a suspended, miraculous moment I'm back in time and I stretch out my hand to find you, expecting to feel your smooth shoulder or a tangled soft mass of hair on the pillow; but then, as my hand closes on air, I remember. I get up, put on my dressing-gown, go to the loo and brush my teeth, then go downstairs to make us both a cup of tea (putting yours in the special cup with the straw), and come along the hall to your room to kiss you good morning and send away the night nurse.

I look at you. As we exchange early-morning pleasantries (How are you? How did you sleep?), I search your dear face for any differences, any new pain or difficulty, and you watch me doing it, giving nothing away. The early-shift nurse will be here soon. Another day begins.

When I'm out – on my way to work, say (part-time: a compromise between your wanting me to live as normal a life as possible and my wanting to be mostly with you), I often run a kind of play in my head, a script. Like this:

Jim: *Listen, you've got to hear the catastrophe that hit us.*

Because it might hit you.

You think that because you're educated, able, independent, you can expect to live a 'normal' life? That you can count on it, make plans that assume that's how life is? Don't you believe it. You're asleep.

If you have your health, your family, and work – you're really fortunate. Admittedly some people seem to stay fortunate all their lives, don't they?

Others don't.

It can change at any time, in just a moment – this afternoon, or tomorrow morning.

Listen to what happened to us, and wake up.

Claire: *Jim, that's not fair. People are living their lives. Just as we were. Just as we are. You can't – browbeat them.*

Jim: *No, but people don't realise how lucky they are when things are just normal. You know? They get upset over nothing. They just don't get it.*

Claire: *What, and you think you can change that – just because you tell them – about us?*

Jim: *It's worth a try, isn't it?*

Claire: *People have to live their lives, Jim.*

Matthew: *Can I interrupt a minute?*

Claire: *Sure, Matt.*

Matthew: *Start at the beginning, Dad. Before I was born, you know, when it was just the two of you.*

Jim: *Okay. Well. So we're students, Claire and I. Claire's a student nurse and I'm doing a geography degree. She'll go on to nursing and I'll go on to teaching. And what with one thing and another – field trips and nursing shifts and essays due in, all that – it's quite an achievement, seeing each other. But I persist, she's this utterly gorgeous tall slim girl, with great long legs and straight black hair she can sit on –*

Matthew: *Wow, could you, Mum?*

Claire: *Yep. But that was a long time ago.*

Jim: *– and the loveliest bright hazel eyes you ever saw, and absolutely everybody loved her –*

Claire: *No they didn't. Can you get a little more real? I was just a girl – like anyone.*

Jim: *You weren't, you were quite different. You saw other people – like you still do – you knew what they needed. How many twenty-year-old girls would've even noticed that wretched old tramp in the rain that time, let alone sat down with him?*

Matthew: *What tramp? I haven't heard that one!*

Jim: *Oh, it's a great story. We were just walking along the road by the shopping centre on the way to catch the bus – we were going somewhere for the* *day, I forget where, so we'd packed sandwiches – and it was bucketing down with rain. Typical for one of our rare days out together! And your mum sees this pretty disgusting old tramp trying to shelter in a doorway, and before I know what's going on she's sat herself down beside him and is patting the pavement next to her for me to sit down too – soaking wet it was – and is pulling out our sandwiches. Bear in mind this old bloke's the real thing – dirty, smelly, awful – and there we are in the pouring rain, eating sandwiches together and chatting about this and that like old friends, until we'd finished – she even left him our thermos of tea. I'll never forget the look he gave her when we got up to go.*

Claire: *That poor man, he needed company. You could see – nobody'd talked to him in ages. He was lonely. He needed reminding – he was a human being.*

Jim: *Well, you certainly did that.*

Matthew: *Love it, Mum! Any other stories like that?*

Jim: *Oh, lots. Your mum was always doing those things. Drove me mad, to be honest – she was always late everywhere. Like that time with the jacket.*

Matthew: *What time with the jacket?*

Jim: *Turned up late without her jacket once – it was a freezing night, just after Christmas – because some girl with a baby needed it more than she did and she had another jacket at home. We missed the start of the concert.*

Claire: *Well, I was right.*

Jim: *I know you were. That's what I mean, though. There wasn't anybody else like you. There still isn't.*

Claire: *There aren't many now. That's for sure. Luckily.*

That's how I imagine the script. All loving and nice – I always loved you, always understood you, always supported you. How could I have done otherwise? Look at what a good person you were! And oh God, you were. You really did sit down with that old tramp; you really did give away your favourite jacket.

The only trouble was, that was *our* special day out you spoiled, that lunch I'd made just for us eaten too early and in the street with a filthy old stranger; the jacket *I'd* bought you, given away on impulse to some other stranger. I remember crying out to you, 'Don't you care for me at all?'

And I remember your tearful reply: 'Oh Jim, I'm so sorry! I wouldn't hurt you for the world, you know that! But we're so lucky, we have each other, and somewhere to live and clothes and enough to eat, and these poor others don't. And they were lovely sandwiches. Wouldn't you *want* to share them with someone who had no joy, nothing to look forward to, like we had? And wherever the jacket is now, nothing can take away the fact that you gave it to me, which is the precious part. And she needed it, Jim!'

'And what about what *I* need? Do you never think of that?'

And so we stumbled on, and we graduated and we married and we had Matt. But things didn't get any better. I resented you, and felt everyone else mattered more to you than I did. I didn't notice the nice things you did for me; only the ones you did for other people. I felt I never knew what you might do next. And you felt trapped and constricted, that I was holding you back, and that I was mean-spirited and selfish. I don't know how it might have resolved itself, but for that particular part of the script which is absolutely true and which I remember word for word:

Claire: *Jim.*

You were feeding Matt in his highchair, concentrating on getting the spoon in at the right moment, scooping up excess stewed apple and banana from around his mouth and popping it back in. I was sitting at the kitchen table marking year eight test papers. It was a Saturday afternoon in June.

Claire: *Jim, there's something going on, with my legs.*

Jim: *Uh-huh?*

I wasn't really listening.

Claire: *Mm. I keep tripping over, or I'll stumble for no reason, and it feels different – my legs feel odd, numb. And I'm getting pins and needles in my hands, and all of a sudden my grip goes.*

The room went still and now you had my full attention. You'd never complained about any physical ailment, ever. You put the spoon down and turned to me with a grave, steady look. You were a trained nurse, and I could see you knew.

Jim: *Oh God, Claire! What is it?*

Claire: *I'm having a load of tests at the hospital this week, but I'm pretty sure it's MS.*

And so now we had something very different to think about, and what I did understand was that whatever was wrong between us simply had to wait. Our world was taken over by appointments, tests, results – but much more crucially by the fact that I now truly didn't know, on a daily basis, what you might do next – what would happen to you next. And that affected us all. I'm not proud of how I was during those dark days.

I think I'll go back to the cleaned-up script, and let Matt join in.

Matthew: *So tell them, Mum. How it was for you.*

Claire: *In the beginning it's a case – of getting round things. Finding – new ways of doing things – to keep your independence. I'd do anything. However hideous. All the things you take for granted – are just taken away from you. Overnight.*

Matthew: *I remember going to school!*

Jim: *Do you, Matt? What do you remember?*

Matthew: *When Mum could walk – well, a bit. You sort of stumbled me to school, Mum, you had those big brown reinforced boots, you used to take my old pushchair to lean on, and you'd have to stop all the time so you made it fun for me – we had pit stops, like racing-car drivers you said, and you'd get out the tube of Smarties. Remember?*

Claire: *Yes. I had to make it fun for me, too.*

Jim: *I remember bedtime.*

Claire: *Which part?*

Jim: *The three quarters of an hour it took you to go upstairs to brush your teeth.*

Claire: *You have to fight. Once you lose – the capacity to do something – you lose it for ever.*

Jim: *You never knew what to expect. What would happen next.*

Claire: *It's like – you're in a fight with a bear.*

Matthew: *What do you mean, a bear?*

Claire: *This huge unpredictable wild thing – so much bigger than you. When you're not looking – it'll swipe out a whole chunk of you – with a single blow. Terrifying. Unexpected. And you never get that chunk back. You're dealing with the loss of that one – and wham! – another blow of the paw – another chunk gone.*

Jim: *Most MS sufferers do at least have remissions, life can be good for years. You were unlucky.*

Claire: *Actually, knowing you have the primary progressive type – concentrates the mind. No messing about. No remissions which might fool you – into thinking things will be ok.*

Jim: *I felt so helpless! I wanted to help you so much!*

Claire: *You did. How could I have fought it – without you? It was the slow degeneration – that was so hard. First, my legs. So, that progression began: sticks. The pushchair. The frame. The wheelchair. But I could still do things – make meals. Write letters. Use the loo. Go out.*

Matthew: *At such cost, though, Mum. I remember.*

I did feel helpless, and I did want to help you. You were so busy simply dealing with each new challenge that perhaps in a way you were protected from the sheer horror of what was happening to you, but I wasn't. And I had horrors of my own to face: not just the possible physical aspects of what my life might become, but the very present ignoble thoughts that sprang into my mind, such as 'well, that's put a stop to her do-gooding stuff, at least.' Oh, Claire!

So I helped you as much out of my guilt as anything else. And it helped me to be able to do something; something good for someone else, like you.

I remember, after we'd had supper and Matt was in his bedroom asleep, we'd often sit on the sofa together for a bit before the long journey to bed. We'd sit with our arms around each other, just clinging on. It wasn't a position we could sustain long without giving you pain, so we moved periodically. We'd cry together. Sometimes we'd talk a little but there really wasn't much to say.

'I'm so scared, Jim. I'm so scared! How bad will it get? It takes me all day just to make the lunch and wash up. I'm so tired. I sleep all the time. The spasms in my legs hurt so much. I can't look after Matt properly. What if my arms go, or my hands? They're already weak, I keep dropping things. What will I become, Jim? What'll happen?'

And of course, I didn't know. What could I say to you? But I could hold you. It was at least a kind of loving.

Claire: *I think – you have to be honest about it. It's vile. You can't help fighting it. But as you realise – you'll never win – it's torture. Losing your hands is the worst. After that you're – completely dependent. You stay where you're put. Can't feed yourself. Can't wipe your nose. Can't scratch an itch.*

Matthew: *You used to say you were 'in tortureland'.*

Jim: *You don't appreciate the implications of weak muscles till it happens to you. Like weak chest muscles mean you can't cough, so if something goes down the wrong way it can cause inflammation, a chest infection, pneumonia.*

The first chest infection was terrifying. Not so much the intravenous antibiotics, the aggressive physiotherapy, even the ventilator – though all of those were frightening. It was the being in hospital instead of at home, and your fear hung in the room. You were so vulnerable, so weak. And once you were back on the ward from intensive care you could never be sure someone would come if you needed anything, because you couldn't press the call bell.

I spent a lot of my time at the hospital during those days. And something shifted in both of us. Here's another bit of real script, from that time. I remember it word for word:

Claire: *Jim, I can't try any more, nothing makes any difference any more, this is it. I'm in bed for the rest of my life, Jim! And how often will we have something like this to deal with? I can't do anything for Matt, or for you. I can't be his mum. I can't be your wife. Jim, please will you go, find someone else? Please, Jim! For his sake, for yours, please!*

Jim: *Darling Claire, you will always be Matt's mum, and you will always be my wife. If I'd known at the beginning, I would still have chosen you. You are my dear beloved girl and you are you – all over, still! Don't push me out! Keep me close, I need you, Claire!*

The look on your face when I said those words is with me always.

They surprised me as much as they surprised you; and they were true. I need you, Claire. I don't want to lose you.

The day I realised that, everything changed.

Matthew: *You know, Dad, you haven't put in any of my bad bits. Like when I ran away because – because –*

Claire: *Because you didn't have – a proper mum. Poor lamb! I remember.*

Matthew: *I'm sorry, Mum.*

Claire: *It was – perfectly understandable. Just scary – for your Dad – and me.*

Jim: *A nightmare. The police were so good, though. And they did find you, quite quickly. It was only three days.*

Claire: *The longest days – of my life.*

Jim: *I'll say. Just as well you put in an appearance at the sweetshop and Brian recognised you.*

Matthew: *And then –*

Jim: *We know, Matt. Don't worry. Do you want to say more? You don't have to.*

Matthew: *Not really. I suppose – what was the worst part for you, Dad?*

Jim: *The fear of infections. Chest infections, urinary infections, and so many miserable other physical problems – not knowing if Mum would pull through, each time.*

Matthew: *Yeah. We really hate hospitals, don't we, Dad?*

Claire: *I'm not that keen – on them myself. But for me – they're not the worst.*

Matthew: *What's your worst?*

Claire: *Feeling as if – I'm a drain on the people I love the most – a nuisance to everybody – utterly worthless.*

Jim: *It's lucky you're not the best judge of your own worth, sweetheart.*

Claire: *And oh, Jim! Thinking that – if only we'd known – we could have done – some of the things we thought we'd do – later, when we had more money. Or time.*

For me, the worst part of hospital is the sheer danger of it: I know that what will probably eventually kill you is an infection your weakened body can no longer resist. As do you, of course.

But for you, the awful part is so often something much more immediate than that, and small – because, for you, the small things are the most cruel. To be able to feel everything just like any of us, only not be able to *do* anything about it! Here's another real bit of script from another hospital stay:

Claire: *I have a funny story for you, Jim.*

Jim: *Oh, what's that?*

Claire: *Late this morning. We hadn't had any nurses round – for a while. So I hadn't been able – to ask anyone. And then this nurse comes in – so I asked her, please would she brush my teeth for me?*

Jim: *And?*

Claire: *And she said – 'I'm not here to brush teeth!' And walked away.*

You laughed about it at the time, but now, whenever you're in hospital, I come in first thing, just to make sure you're comfortable.

Matthew: *Are we on to now, then, Dad?*

Jim: *Sure, Matt. Your 'now': start of year nine. Thirteen and – oh, a couple of months. Everything to play for. Right?*

Matthew: *Yeah, but I didn't mean that. I like that we're always together. Most of my friends, their parents are never around. Their dads work long hours. Their mums are always out. You're always there for me, Mum. I'll come home from school, we'll chat, you always want to know about my day, you always remember everything. If something good happens, I can't wait to come and tell you. If something bad happens, you always help. And with my homework, you help!*

Claire: *Honey, of course I do. Any mum does that.*

Jim: *Firstly, no, they don't; and secondly, see what a great mum you are? You do all the important things.*

Matthew: *And Dad and me, we do lots together. For Mum, and for just us. I know we're lots closer than my friends' families. I've learned a lot, too. I like doing things for you, Mum. I know how to do lots of things my friends can't do.*

Claire: *You make a mean spaghetti Bolognese.*

The cleaned-up script is true, of course. Well, sort of – as far as it goes. It just misses out the bad bits I can't bear to think about. So we might as well continue with it for just for a while longer, because for you, Claire – well, for you, it's not so far off true, at that.

Matthew: *How is now for you then, Mum?*

Claire: *It sounds silly. But there's a reason for this. I don't know what that is. But I've had a lot of time – to think. I've learned a lot from it.*

Matthew: *Like what?*

Claire: *Like how beautiful the world is – when you have time to really look at it. The ordinary things – that aren't ordinary at all. Flowers. Sunsets. Rain. Your heart just fills with joy. I have lots of time to look. And people – how much you can do for people – just by listening to them. I have time to listen. I'm almost always at home. I can open the door – with the control system. And people seem to find it helps – to chat to me.*

Jim: *I think half the neighbourhood comes round in any given week. And of course they love coming – you're so interested in everyone, in their families, in what's going on.*

Claire: *Well. I am interested.*

Jim: *Exactly, that's my point. You might be forgiven for dwelling on your own problems, but you don't. And you're honest and straightforward when people do ask about you, so they feel – well, part of the family, on the inside. Friends.*

Claire: *They are friends. People are lovely. I think that if I hadn't had this – of course things would have been – different. But it might not have been – a difference for the better.*

Jim: *Oh, Claire! How can you say so? Look at you!*

Claire: *Well, yes. I can use my mouth. Suck through a straw. Talk. I can see still, so I can look. On good days – I can move my head a little. Oh, and breathe. But that's it.*

Matthew: *You can only take slow, little breaths, though, Mum.*

Claire: *That's true. I can't speak and breathe – at the same time – like you. I breathe in first – then speak on the out breath. I choose my words.*

Matthew: *And you can only eat soft food, we have to purée everything. Or something might go down the wrong way. That must be pretty boring for you.*

Claire: *Even so. Without this – we might not have loved each other – so much.*

So that's the clean script. The one I tell myself as I go about my outside life, when I'm away from you.

And you know, I imagine our marriage as being something like a mobius strip – like taking a narrow length of paper, twisting it once and then sticking the two ends together: two sides, but only one surface.

Because you're still 'doing good', my precious girl. Only now I can be part of it – I know my place in it.

But also there is the underneath, the place where it will never stop hurting. I know what that place is for you.

And at those times I just hold you. What else can I do? It is at least a kind of loving.

10. *Living*

BE FREE

'One of the teachers of the law ... asked him,
"Of all the commandments, which is the most important?"
"The most important one," answered Jesus, "is this: Hear,
O Israel, the Lord our God, the Lord is one. Love the Lord
your God with all your heart and with all your soul and with
all your mind and with all your strength. The second is this:
love your neighbour as yourself."'

Mark 12:28-31

Margaret approached the two steps up to her front door with some difficulty. It was a nuisance, being old; but some days were worse than others, and this was one of those. She concentrated on the careful placing of her stick, pushed herself up onto the first step, bumped her shopping-trolley up beside her, and paused to catch her breath. Then she repeated the process with the second step. She leaned on the stick and the trolley handle, breathing in short, shallow gasps.

The young man from the house next door, crouched over bits of motorbike laid out along the cracked cement path among the weeds, looked up at her briefly, then turned back to his own concerns.

He hadn't thought of her, and now the idea took root. Of course! The old dear probably had quite a lot stashed away, and it looked as if she'd lived in that house for years and years – should be a cinch to break into, he'd give the job to Larry, good experience for the lad. Next door's exactly the same layout as here, he thought, and what with his living here and knowing the house, and with the old dear next door probably deaf as a post, it should be easy – he can just do the downstairs and get out.

Finding good targets was getting harder, and the houses round here were mostly run down now, like his – not worth the trouble. But then again, the cops mostly didn't bother either, so it was a good area for a base, if not to work in.

Larry and Mel were out now. They had a great mother-and-son routine going, worked a treat. They generally used the old trick of one engaging the householder downstairs with the other rifling upstairs; and they were good, no one ever knew till after they were long gone. Though it had to be said that people were getting more suspicious and less likely even to open the door, especially a woman at home on her own – more often than not, now, even if Larry and Mel insisted they needed to dial 999 she'd ask them to wait outside while she dialled it for them, whatever story they'd spun her.

Bloody nuisance, it was. And pick-pocketing was less lucrative than it used to be – people were more careful, they carried less about with them, times were harder. So although breaking and entering was risky, he'd thought for a while that it was the way to go; it had been quite productive recently.

Course, what you wanted was the real job: a van, overalls and clipboards, walk in bold as brass and take the stuff out in broad daylight, signed for and everything, like you were some real company; but that cost money and needed good organisation, fences and that to handle the goods – he was nowhere near that level yet. Plus the lads didn't have the brains or the cool for it. He needed to train them up first.

So the old lady next door was perfect.

Margaret dug her purse out of her coat pocket, took out her key and opened the front door. It was stiff and you had to wiggle it a certain way – awkward for her arthritic fingers, but the front door was only one of many things that needed looking at in her house, and at her age she was inclined to let things go till there was no alternative.

It was true, she thought ruefully as she worked her way down the hallway and into the kitchen to put the kettle on, that her house was now shabby. It was basically sound, but it badly needed a coat of paint – several! – and she couldn't bear the thought of the fuss and disruption. It was like having window locks fitted – just one of those things that didn't seem to matter, really. 'Well', she'd say to acquaintances, 'I'm ninety-two and I've lived here perfectly happily for more years than I care to remember, so why bother now?'

The trouble with that attitude, however, was that it meant she didn't have an odd-job man lined up for when she did need something small done – like the loose tile on the top step which had been loose for ages and today had finally come adrift altogether. She'd been avoiding it for months, she knew it was there; but someone else – the postman, say – might step on it and go flying. She realised she really would have to find someone to sort it out, soon.

Over the years a kind neighbour had usually done that kind of thing for her, but people had moved away and she didn't know anyone on the estate any more. It had gone downhill a lot, to tell you the truth. Take the young people who lived next door; she'd seen a total of six families in that house, but now it was more like a student let – lots of comings and goings – and none of them had been there long.

In fact they were all ages, really, but it was the young fair lad she ached for when she saw him go past her front window. He looked as if he should still be at school, but clearly, he wasn't. He looked lost. She wondered what response she'd get if she baked a cake and went round with it? A few years ago she would have done it without a further thought, but the last time she'd gone round to someone with a cake – to the neighbour across the street – she'd got such a blank stare from her that she'd realised such a gesture wasn't always welcome. Not nowadays, anyway.

She made her cup of tea and took it carefully through to the sitting-room. She sat down with it, thinking about next door. Were they a family, she wondered? Somehow she thought not. The young man with the motorbike was mostly there during the day, so presumably he didn't have work. The middle-aged woman and the fair lad often came and went together, but without any regular pattern that she could see; then there was a pretty slim girl with long dark hair and a West Indian lad and a thin older man she instinctively distrusted, and several others – she lost track – she knew they didn't all live there.

What would become of the young ones, what sort of life were they living? She looked around at her familiar, rather crowded sitting room: the room she mostly lived in these days, and slept in, too, sometimes, since the sofa was perfectly comfortable, on those evenings when she couldn't summon the energy to climb the stairs.

It was a room which bore testimony to a long life of travel, friendships and many interests; the travel, she had found, not so much broadening the mind as deepening one's compassion for other people. She had come to love the stranger in a hundred unfamiliar guises, and admire profoundly the courage and humility which others brought to their sometimes appalling circumstances. She knew herself to be fortunate indeed.

The world was so fascinating – she was grateful for the education which had given her an entry into history, other cultures, the vast horizons of geographies different from her own: deserts, lagoons, volcanoes. In her room there were glowing pieces of glass from Murano, bark paintings from Mexico, rugs from Turkey, African woodcarvings – oh, so much more, and all evoking luminous memories of the dear friends with whom they had been chosen, or by whom they had been given.

Her eyes rested comfortably and naturally on the object she loved most: the Victorian skeleton clock on the mantelpiece, her husband's first gift to her when they were little more than children, bought with his first pay cheque 'because the proportions are so beautiful, Margaret, I thought – well, a maths teacher, you know, you could look at it and get things back into perspective, if the school day had been tough.' Dear John! How often, through the years, had she done just that? For much longer, now, than all the years that he had lived.

Not that he had known it – and Margaret realised that she had never had occasion to tell him – but the proportions were indeed beautiful because they conformed to the golden ratio: the perfect relationship between height and width that underlies the structure of most living things and of a great deal of art – the Parthenon in Athens, for example. Some years previously she had visited the Parthenon, and had returned with a large print showing the west face which she had hung on the wall next to the clock. She enjoyed sitting quietly studying the golden ratio displayed in two such different things. How interesting the world was!

The young people next door, though – that school-age lad, say – had his parents or teachers encouraged him to love beautiful things, as hers had? Had he been taught at school something of the astonishing structures of the world he lived in? She supposed that these things were still taught at private schools, but the lad next door wouldn't have gone to one of those. The comprehensive down the road was regularly lambasted in the local paper – not something, she felt, calculated to help it improve, if improvement were needed. But she had to admit the children she saw trailing out of it when she happened to be passing at the end of the school day didn't inspire confidence. It wasn't that they were rough or rude, although they were sometimes those things. It was the empty look in their eyes, the apparently aimless drifting along while listening to something through an earpiece, the endless playing of electronic games (a neighbour's boy had shown her, once), which saddened her. She thought these children were lonelier than her generation had been, and more isolated from the world around them.

Perhaps she was simply wrong. She was, after all, an old woman.

A couple of nights later, it was cold. Margaret wasn't feeling very well and she thought she'd stay downstairs in the sitting room for the night, and not embark on the long trek upstairs to a cold bedroom. She always slept perfectly well on the sofa, and she always had sheets and blankets folded up at one end with a nightie and dressing-gown, for just this eventuality.

So she made up the bed and, round about nine o'clock, settled down with a hot drink and a book. By nine thirty she'd turned out the light.

She was woken by the sound of a sharp intake of breath, though as she surfaced she didn't realise that was what it had been. She became aware that there was somebody else in the room; and that there was some kind of localised light.

Margaret wasn't afraid, but she wanted to know what was happening. So she lay still for a moment, listening. Somebody was standing just on the other side of the sofa, behind her, holding a torch; the light had picked out the clock on the mantelpiece facing her and, as she woke, had swung across slightly to include the picture beside it. The person was breathing in short, sharp bursts but was otherwise very still. It sounded like a man's breathing. She knew that if he but looked down, over the back of the sofa, he'd see her.

But he wasn't looking down.

For what seemed like hours but must have only been a minute or two, Margaret listened to the breathing, and waited. The torchlight was steady on the clock and the picture. Then quite suddenly the man moved round the sofa right past her and went to stand in front of the mantelpiece with his back to her, training the torch first on the clock, then on the picture. It was the young fair lad from next door, and he had a black bin sack in one hand.

'It's the same!' he murmured. 'The same!'

Margaret felt for her dressing-gown and concentrated all her attention on what was needed to get up and walk to the door without being heard. Painfully, she eased her arms into the sleeves of the dressing-gown, lowered her feet onto the carpet, and stood, leaning on the arm of the sofa. She moved slowly towards the door, taking little steps and trying to breathe silently. The young man was so absorbed he didn't notice, and Margaret got there, unobserved.

She said clearly and calmly, 'Don't be afraid, I'm switching on the light,' and did so.

The lad whirled around, his eyes huge, little blotches of acne and incipient beard standing out unnaturally in his white face like the newly-exposed ruts of a snowy field after a thaw. He shifted his weight, ready to run.

Margaret said again, 'Don't be afraid. I won't hurt you and I'm not angry.'

For a moment they looked at each other, he poised to make a dash for it, she standing still and, she realised, blocking his escape. She said, 'I'm going to sit down in this armchair,' and moved slowly away from the door. 'You said "it's the same,"' she said. 'I'm interested. What's the same? What did you see?'

The lad licked his dry lips. 'Dunno. Nothing,' he said, and then, seeing his chance, he swept the clock off the mantelpiece into his sack and ran for the door. He flung it open, wrestled for a sickening moment with the front door two strides away down the hallway, then pulled it open and slammed it shut behind him in a desperate bid to delay pursuit.

He spun round to run, slipped on the broken tile and smashed awkwardly down the next step and onto the path. When he tried to get to his feet he almost blacked out from the surge of pain up his right leg. He tried again, more cautiously, and stopped at once, retching. He realised, terrified, that he couldn't move.

Down at the police station some ten minutes later, PC Cox put down the phone and called over to PC Blake at the desk in the next room, 'Oy Fred! Remember we were waiting for that reason to go down the Fairfield estate and show our faces? Just come up. That woman Sue Digby who calls up all the time.'

'What, the one who's always on about the bloke across the road revving his bike at night, uses her front garden as a toilet on his way home from the local? That one?'

'That's the one. Become quite a mate of mine she has, one way and another, the amount of time I spend with her on the phone.' PC Cox looked at his watch and reluctantly got to his feet. 'Come on then, s'pose we'd better get on down there.'

Once they were in the car PC Cox said, 'That woman's got it in for him, right enough! I tell her we can't be going out for every bloke that gets caught short in the wrong place, and she tells me it isn't just that, she don't like the look of him, nor of the others that come and go in his house!' They both laughed. 'Bout once a week, we have this conversation. I tell her we can't be going after everybody some other person don't like the look of neither, especially round there. She'd be better off getting some proof of something wrong, I told her. So, she's been at the old curtains, spying on 'em.'

'Blimey, she should get a life.'

'Yeah, except that she reckons one of 'em's just tried to burgle the old lady next door, only he's hurt his leg or something and can't get up and he's right there on the old dear's front path right now, so maybe she's come up with the goods after all. At least it'll get her off my back for a bit, with luck.'

'She's not standing out there waiting or anything, is she?'

'No, I told her to keep inside and not give us any complications. Told her I'll call her in the morning.'

Larry sweated with pain and tried to think. Dan had gone round the pub on his bike, and he knew he wouldn't be back till after closing time. That was hours off yet. Some of the others were out too, it was anyone's guess when they'd be home – maybe before Dan, though. He'd left his mobile charging in the kitchen – how stupid was that! He could remember thinking 'that's ok, I'm only going next door, won't be more than half an hour, max.' But who would've thought the old lady would be sleeping downstairs, instead of where she belonged, upstairs in her bed?

Luckily this bit of road was fairly quiet, and if he kept dead still till one of the others came home, maybe he'd get away with it. As long as the old lady herself didn't think to look out! Somehow he thought she wouldn't, but you never knew. He closed his eyes and breathed in slowly. Jesus, but it hurt!

'Well, would you take a look at this then?'

Larry's eyes snapped open. Two police officers were standing over him, grinning.

Oblivious to Larry's difficulty, Margaret had made herself a cup of tea and taken it back to bed with her. She was sorting out her emotions, which were confused. Her clock! He'd taken her clock! She should have been feeling outrage, surely, fear ... but she realised that, just as when she'd first seen him she had been neither afraid nor angry, she still wasn't, even now. How strange! The truth was that, even though he had broken into her house, she had not at any point thought of him as a threat. She had previously thought of him as the lad who lived next door, and, she realised, she did so still. Not a thief: just a child, a boy she'd felt concerned about.

And now what she mostly felt with regard to him was, apparently, excitement.

Only a natural mathematician would see proportion and ratio the way she was sure that he had, without being taught it. Such a natural understanding was most rare; she had encountered it perhaps two or three times in her whole teaching career, and never in someone so untaught. 'It's the same!' he'd said. Clearly he hadn't seen that relationship before, and equally clearly it had stunned him. To have such a mind, and no knowledge with which to furnish it! She ached to teach him.

She sat with her hands around her cup, warming them, thinking about it. After the initial thrill of recognition, the real question was simply practical: how should she go about it? What should she do?

Without a doubt the best thing for him would be if somebody else taught him; somebody teaching now, in some good school. He needed to get back to school. Whom did she still know who could help?

When her doorbell rang she was so engrossed in these thoughts that, after working her way to the front door and opening it, she just gaped at the police officer standing on her doorstep. She realised she hadn't taken in a word he'd said.

'I'm sorry?'

The officer stepped aside and gestured towards the path behind him, where his colleague was crouched on the ground with an arm around the shoulders of the boy from next door, who looked white.

'Oh, what happened?' Margaret peered out in agitation. 'Is he hurt?'

'Broke his ankle, probably. We've called for an ambulance, shouldn't be long.' The officer smiled at her. 'Bit of luck, that fall, caught him red-handed. We think this might be yours.' He bent down and picked up her clock from the top step. 'He must have cushioned it when he fell, doesn't look damaged.'

'Oh no,' Margaret said, 'that's his. I gave it to him, didn't I?' she said, smiling at Larry.

'You what?'

'Gave it to him. Only he left in such a hurry he forgot to take the picture that goes with it. Will you come and help me take it down, officer, then he can take them both with him?'

PC Cox opened his mouth, then shut it.

'You trying to tell me he didn't break in and take this?'

'We met as friends.'

'What, at this time of night?' PC Cox's incredulous look had begun to change into something more like suspicion. Smoothly, Margaret took the situation in hand. She looked PC Cox straight in the eye and said, 'Well, we're neighbours, after all! And young people are up at all hours, aren't they? I'm an old woman, officer, I keep odd hours myself. You don't need the sleep you used to, at my age.'

She hobbled down onto the path and looked at Larry. He gazed back at her with a mixture of – what? Amazement, anxiety, disbelief? She couldn't read it in the poor light of her porch lamp. She said gently, 'Just you get that ankle seen to, and then we'll talk some more. What you saw was right, do you hear? It was right! And we're going to have such fun exploring it.'

The following morning, when Sue Digby got her promised phone call and heard PC Cox's account of the previous night's events, she burst into tears, which surprised them both.

'She's good, she is!' Sue said. 'Know what she done when I moved in here? Come round with a cake! Nobody never done that for me before, didn't know what to say to her.'

'That was nice.'

'I ent never forgotten it. She don't deserve that scum next door. She never really give him her clock and her picture, did she?'

'She did. I took the picture off the wall myself, put 'em both in the sack for him. He took 'em to A&E in the ambulance with him and all – wouldn't be parted from that sack. And your bloke what you keep going on about – he come home on his bike as the lad were being lifted into the ambulance, so he got to hear all about it too.'

PC Cox grinned, shaking his head. 'Amazing! Blow me if he didn't go and have a look at the step the lad fell over – apparently a tile was broken, or something. Said he'd be round in the morning to fix it!'

Sue Digby gave a little shriek down the phone. 'He never did!'

'Honest!' In the cold light of morning, yesterday night seemed even more extraordinary than before; and to PC Cox, Sue Digby suddenly felt like an old friend.

'You know what? I reckon you'll be seeing some changes down your end of town.'

Notes and Questions

I'm not a theologian, and this was never intended to be a work of scholarship; so these notes are no more than nudges that may be helpful. If they aren't, please ignore them!

Scripture is living, by which I mean it *does* things in us. I aim to do no more here than 'place' the Bible verse in question. [1]

I would be delighted if this book leads you to explore the Bible more deeply if you don't already know it well; and if you do, I hope so much that you will enjoy teasing out the threads of the story I have told in the light of the Scripture that you know.

I hope that the stories will lead you into fruitful journeys. I trust that there will be resonances in them all which have nothing to do with themes or any kind of 'set' projects or study but which are simply personal to you.

On the other hand you may wish to use the book in church house groups, or *The Golden Bird*, say, as a starting-point for a discussion on abortion, or *Amy's Visit* as an introduction to a session on counselling or working in prisons; I will be so pleased if you find the stories helpful in this way.

But however you approach them, I hope you enjoy them.

[1] My scripture notes draw heavily on the NIV Study Bible's footnotes, on Tom Wright's 'For Everyone' series and on Richard Burridge's *Four Gospels, One Jesus?*, all of which I gladly acknowledge (see Bibliography).

Where I quote a different book of the Bible from the one under discussion, I give the full reference (eg Deuteronomy 6:4, that is, the Book of Deuteronomy, chapter 6, verse 4); and where I quote from elsewhere within the same book I give just the chapter and verse (eg 1:15).

1. The Real Thing (Slow down)

My point of departure for this story was the following Bible passage:

'The wise heart will know the proper time and procedure.' *Ecclesiastes 8:5*

The Bible verse: Ecclesiastes is a book written by an old man (possibly King Solomon) looking back over his life and seeing that even what wise and knowledgeable people do is 'meaningless, a 'chasing after the wind' (1:15), without God. In his long life he has sought wisdom and has watched how men live on the earth, but he concludes that even the wisest man cannot understand either wisdom or man's destiny, and that the work of people on earth is to receive with gratitude what God gives and to enjoy it while they can: 'go, eat your food with gladness, and drink your wine with a joyful heart, for it is now that God favours what you do' (9:7). And in that doing 'there is a time for everything' (3:1), and the wise heart will know when that is, and how to go about it.

So what makes for a wise heart? To begin with such a heart must feel that timing and good procedure are important, or it wouldn't be looking out for them; and consequently it will watch and pay attention, otherwise it would not be able to judge when or how to do a thing. And that takes time. So a wise heart will, before anything, go slowly.

It isn't possible either to love anyone (including yourself), or to engage with the world around you if you live in a rush all the time, and mostly, in the West, we do. To learn to love – ourselves, each other, and the creation around us – we have to slow right down.

Think about whether you've noticed the simple things around you recently: your food, the weather, the scenery, your clothes, your home. Have you enjoyed them, or just rushed through them, ignored them or 'dealt with' them?

Think about your friends and the people dearest to you. These are your treasures; have you enjoyed being with them recently, or do months go by with you 'always meaning' to call or write?

When you're with others, do you pay attention, listening to what they're saying, noticing their expression, really hearing what they're telling you? Or is your mind often elsewhere?

How did you describe the characteristics of a wise heart? Think of someone you know whom you would say has a wise heart, and think about why they came to mind.

'The wise heart will know the proper time and procedure' for what? Here the context is, significantly, acts of obedience; and reading through Ecclesiastes, which is quite short, takes you on a marvellous journey of what is, and isn't, wisdom, both in terms of people's behaviour as such and that behaviour in relation to God.

The story: Who in this story would you say has a wise heart?

What does that person do to demonstrate this?

Ask the questions you asked yourself earlier – about noticing the food and the scenery and engaging with those around you – for the person with the wise heart whom you identified in the story.

Were the answers different from what they were for you?

2. *Flying* (Listen)

My point of departure for this story was the following Bible passage:

'My sheep listen to my voice; I know them, and they follow me.'

John 10:27

The Bible verse: This verse comes at the end of a long discussion between Jesus and the Jews as to whether he is or is not the Messiah, which Jesus roots in his relationship with his Father, challenging the Jews in their claim that they are sons of God and Abraham.

'Why is my language not clear to you?' asks Jesus (8:43). 'Because you are unable to hear what I say ... the reason you do not hear is that you do not belong to God.' There follows the story of the healing of the man born blind which demonstrates Jesus's relationship with his Father in action (the man born blind echoing Jesus's frustration with the Jews when they repeatedly ask him to explain what happened to him: 'I have told you already and you did not listen. Why do you want to hear it again?'). And following this healing is the chapter on the good shepherd.

The connection between the two may not be obvious to us, but it would have been abundantly clear to the Jews, for whom God was the Shepherd of Israel (as for example in the beginning of psalm 23, 'The Lord is my shepherd, I shall not want'), and the longed-for Messiah the great shepherd of the sheep, as his father King David had been, and as prophesied by the prophet Ezekiel (Ezekiel 34:23). Jesus is claiming the authority of God, and that it is through that authority that he healed the man born blind and performed all the other 'signs'. The Jews understand him perfectly and ask him straight out, 'If you are the Christ, tell us plainly.' Jesus replies, 'I did tell you, but you do not believe ... because you are not my sheep.'

There is an interesting sequence in this verse: Jesus says his sheep listen to his voice, and he knows them, and they follow him. You would expect 'My sheep listen to my voice; they know me, and they follow me.' But at the centre of this verse is Jesus's knowledge of *them.* It is his knowledge of them that builds their trust in him, from which comes the fact that they listen to his voice and, having heard it, follow him. The logic of the verse is as it were circular, it has no beginning and no end; the identity of the sheep is rooted in the identity of the shepherd, which is what John's gospel is all about.

To listen, to God, to each other and to ourselves, is the beginning of relationship and changes everything.

Think about how you listen in each of those three areas.

How do you listen to yourself? If you're on your own, and don't immediately fill the vacuum by turning on the the radio or the television, how you feel? Do you normally respect those feelings, or quash them? What do you think would happen if you paid attention to them?

How do you feel when somebody else really listens to you?

Do you think you listen to other people well?

How can you listen to God?

The story: Think about how the various characters in this story listen to each other. Is it easy for them?

Does the manner in which they listen change during the course of the story? How does this affect their relationships?

Think about Joe. How do you think his life, and the lives of those around him, may be affected in the future because somebody listened to him?

3. *The Golden Bird* (Imagine)

My point of departure for this story was the following Bible passage:

'Now to him who is able to do immeasurably more than all we ask or imagine, according to his power that is at work within us, to him be glory in the church and in Christ Jesus throughout all generations for ever and ever! Amen.'

Ephesians 3:20

The Bible verse: The first half of Paul's letter to the Ephesians is a celebration of God's work of reconciliation by grace for us through Christ, and the second half calls us to respond. The verse comes at the very end of the first half, an outpouring of praise for all that has gone before, that God might be glorified 'in the church and in Christ Jesus throughout all generations for ever!'

Gentiles and Jews have been united 'through the blood of Christ' to form one church, and the beautiful description of how Jesus became our peace by destroying the barriers between us on the cross, 'creating in himself one new man out of the two,' is here in Ephesians (2:14-18). It is his vast love – 'how wide and long and high and deep' – through which God can do immeasurably more than we can ask or imagine, and Paul sees that work in a context of unity and reconciliation.

The imagination is transformative and more powerful than we can conceive. Moreover, because it is intuitive, God can use it to break down the limitations we impose on ourselves to retain control, and take us to places we had never dreamed of.

But more than anything the imagination is *creative,* and as such draws us into God's constant work of creation all around us. We, being made in his image as well as being a part of the creation ourselves, join with him in his creative process whether we agree, or are aware of it, or not.

How willing are you to let him into your imagination? The extent of what God does in and through us is according to the measure of his power at work within us, the letter to the Ephesians tells us. This is an encouraging reminder that when we see God at work in our lives, it is *his* work achieved through *his* power. Does that give you hope?

The story: This is a story about two young girls who allow their imaginations room to work. What is the outcome for both of them? Do you think that something as 'ordinary' as a dead leaf really could have such a profound effect on someone's life?

Was it the dead leaf alone that made the difference?

4. *Amy's Visit* (Forgive)

My point of departure for this story was the following Bible passage:

Then Peter came to Jesus and asked, 'Lord, how many times shall I forgive my brother when he sins against me? Up to seven times?' Jesus answered, 'I tell you, not seven times, but seventy-seven times.'

Matthew 18: 21,22

The Bible verse: This verse comes in the fourth of five big blocks of teaching or discourses around which Matthew builds his gospel, aiming to present Jesus as the great teacher of Israel. This section chiefly concerns teaching for how the church should conduct herself – with humility and love, her members respecting one another and forgiving each other. Jesus tells Peter that he must forgive his brother either seventy-seven times or seventy times seven times, depending on the translation; either is a lot! It looks as if Jesus puts no limit on our capacity or willingness to forgive.

God is working in and through us, but he calls us to join him in that work; and chief among those things which he asks us to do, with the help of his grace and power, is to forgive others their sins against us.

Forgiveness is the key to healthy relationship, and we must learn to do it, or we will not ourselves be forgiven. But also, to the extent that we hold on to injuries done to us, to that extent we ourselves are bound and imprisoned: 'dead in our sins'. We *must* forgive, every bit for our own sake as for those of others.

How, though? It's good to know we are never expected to do this by ourselves. Jesus Christ made it possible when he took responsibility for our sins on the cross and forgave those who had put him there. Now, as St Benedict says, we can request the help of his grace to accomplish what we cannot do for ourselves by nature. As Paul points out, we can forgive others because God first forgave us (Colossians 3:13).

Consider the work of forgiveness that is still outstanding in your life. Is there anyone already alongside you who can help?

The story: Why do you think Amy was in a home? What was wrong with her?

What did Jen do to make it possible for Amy to come to a place where she could forgive what had been done to her? Do you think it was important for Amy to be able to forgive? Why?

5. *Jack's Gift* (See what is there)

My point of departure for this story was the following Bible passage:

'The eye is the lamp of the body. If your eyes are good, your whole body will be full of light. But if your eyes are bad, your whole body will be full of darkness. If then the light within you is darkness, how great is that darkness!'

Matthew 6: 22,23

The Bible verse: This passage from Matthew's gospel is part of the Sermon on the Mount, the first of the five great discourses. It comes towards the end of a long section, beginning with the beatitudes, in which Jesus raises the bar of ethical behaviour to apparently impossible heights ('you have heard it was said ... do not murder ... but I tell you that anyone who is angry with his brother will be subject to judgement', etc – 5: 21, 22). He goes on to teach his disciples how to pray and how to develop a healthy spiritual life, and it is in this context that the passage about the eyes being the lamp of the body comes.

This raises questions about how we see things. Light and darkness are more a theme in the gospel of John than of Matthew, but significantly this passage in Matthew follows Jesus's staement in the previous chapter 'You are the light of the world ... let your light so shine before men, that they may see your good deeds and praise your Father in heaven' (5: 14,16). The passage makes a further connection regarding light: it implies that how we see things, how we process what we see, has a direct result on whether we are full of light or full of darkness – which, of course, directly affects those with whom we come into contact.

And the passage implies we have a choice in the matter: we can choose how we use our eyes. This whole section is full of admonitions ('when you give to the needy, do not announce it with trumpets ... when you pray, do not be like the hypocites ... when you fast, do not look sombre ... do not store up for yourselves treasures on earth ... do not worry ... do not judge ... ' etc). Things happen, even awful things, but we have a choice in how we respond.

Suppose you cannot forgive or let go? Nursing bitterness is deadly. It destroys love and makes it impossible to see anyone clearly; we end up seeing everyone else through the warped lens of our own grief and pain.

To what extent do you think our experiences colour our thoughts and affect our judgements?

Can we help it?

The story: Think about each character in this story – the shoppers, Paul, Jack, Sal. What do they see, and what do they fail to see? What are the consequences?

Do you think Jack had a gift? If so, what was it?

Why was Paul unable to see anything worthwhile in Jack?

Why couldn't the shoppers see that the toys were the same?

Do you think there's any hope for Paul? For Jack?

6. *The Phone Call* (Live in the present)

My point of departure for this story was the following Bible passage:

'I tell you, now is the time of God's favour, now is the day of salvation.'

2 Corinthians 6:2

The Bible verse: St Paul's second letter to the Corinthians was written to encourage the people to stand firm in what they had learned from Paul, and not to be persuaded by false teachers who were attacking his teaching and his reputation. He quotes to them God's promise from the book of Isaiah (Isaiah 49:8-16) – 'In the time of my favour I will answer you, and and in the day of salvation I will help you,' and in this verse declares to them that that day of restoration and joy has come; it is now.

We so often don't live in the present moment, and yet that is the only place that is real, and the only place in which we can find God; he is always only there.

Do you wish yourself into the past (when you were happy), or into the future (when you will be free of this or that constraint)? Or do you take elements of your present life (a particular person, say) and weave yourself an imagined scenario around them, which you try to inhabit?

We've all tried such ways of avoiding the grit of the present moment, in which we actually find ourselves.

'Now' is the only time in which you can do anything, so have a look at it. Quite often some feeling, fear or issue will surface, and this is a useful exercise:

Sit down with it and really look at it. *Feel* it. What exactly does it feel like? Where is it coming from? If it had a name, what would that name be? When you can bring it close, what does it look like? And, where is it now?

The story: Think about Kate and Maggie, and why their lives took the courses that they did. Do you think that Kate could have done anything differently? Could Maggie?

Is it too late for Kate?

How do you think she might move forward now? If she was to do three things straight away, what might they be?

7. *Buttercups* (Love the earth)

My point of departure for this story was the following Bible passage:

'The earth is the Lord's, and everything in it, the world, and all who live in it; for he founded it upon the seas and established it upon the waters.'

Psalm 24: 1,2

The Bible verse: This psalm of David was either written for the occasion when King David brought the Ark of the Covenant into Jerusalem for the first time, or for a festival which commemorated that event. God had led him into victory over his enemies in battle, and this is a great shout of praise and joy, giving God the glory for what he has done and for who he is – the Creator of everything, the King of glory, the Lord Almighty.

In an agricultural society like the Old Testament Middle East, people would have understood more deeply than we do their intimate connection to the earth from which they drew what they needed for life; and from bitter experience of the effects of a poor or a lost harvest, would have felt both more dependent on God on a daily basis, and more thankful when the harvest was good.

Although this is still the lot of thousands of our brothers and sisters around the world, we in the West are generally protected from the direct results of poor harvests or other natural disasters. But we are part of the earth and intimately connected to it all the same – created things like the plants and the animals. We can't live separated from them, nor should we try.

Think about the earth we live in: your native country, and those parts of it which carry a particular significance for you; other countries you love, or about which you are concerned; the place you live in now.

Close your eyes and run past them in your mind, like a film, any photographs of the natural world and of people which mean something to you: volcanoes, deserts, canyons, waterfalls; tigers, lizards, butterflies; other countries' children.

It's easy to feel overwhelmed by the vast needs of whole countries torn by famine or war or the ruin caused by natural disasters, but we are not generally called to serve on that scale. Generally our part is smaller. What can we do? The earth is the Lord's, but we are his stewards; so, what do our gifts and experience fit us for? When you run that 'film' before your eyes, is there an issue or picture that tugs particularly at your heart?

The story: Why do you think Stanley became the adult he did? Why do you think Bridget was able to connect with him?

Imagine how the story carries on beyond the place where I have finished it. What is Stanley doing now? What has changed in him? What effects on others might there be?

8. The Echoes of Pain (Be kind)

My point of departure for this story was the following Bible passage:

'Therefore as God's chosen people, holy and dearly loved, clothe yourselves with compassion, kindness, humility, gentleness and patience.'

Colossians 3:12

The Bible verse: This passage from Paul's letter to the church at Colossae appeals to the people, once they have given up their old 'philosophy' and embraced Jesus as their true Lord, to live according to what Jesus commands.

Don't submit to the world's rules, says Paul, they are all 'destined to perish with use, because they are based on human commands and teachings' (2:22).

What does it mean to be kind? How can we serve one another in the everyday things of life?

The qualities that are described here – compassion, kindness, humility, gentleness and patience – take *time.* It takes time to pay attention to other people, and to respond to them with compassion, gentleness, patience: which leads us back to the business of slowing down and living in the present moment.

In addition, however, these qualities are here asked of those who know themselves to be holy and dearly loved. In other words, they are asked of people who are God's beloved: God loves us first, that we, being secure in his unfailing and unconditional love for us, may risk loving others as he loves us.

There are at least two reasons for doing this: firstly, Jesus commands us to do it ('my command is this: love each other as I have loved you' (John 15:12) – no ducking that!), and secondly, you never know the importance to someone else of what you considered the most casual word or kindness.

The story: How would you describe Joan? What effect did her childhood experience have on her adult self?

What did Joan's old shoes represent to her? Why did she feel the need to 'punish' her feet?

What did the young man in the shop do that demonstrated compassion, kindness, humility, gentleness and patience?

What did he do for Joan?

9. *The Bear* (Be dependent)

My point of departure for this story was the following Bible passage:

Then Jesus declared ... 'All that the Father gives me will come to me, and whoever comes to me I will never drive away. For I have come down from heaven not to do my will but to do the will of him who sent me.'

John 6:37- 38

The Bible verse: This verse comes early on in John's gospel just after Jesus has fed the five thousand, walked on the water and declared 'I am the bread of life', the first of the seven great 'I Am' statements that declare his identity. He roots himself in God his Father, without whom, he says, he can do nothing (5:19, 30). The Jews understand very well that he is 'making himself equal with God' and try to kill him, and it is in this context and atmosphere of tension that Jesus continues to elaborate on the meaning of his being the bread of life: that whoever believes in the one his Father has sent and eats his flesh will be raised by him at the last day – a 'hard teaching' that causes many of his disciples to stop following him.

The Father's will is paramount – 'all that the Father gives me will come to me,' and the Son is entirely obedient to that will – 'and whoever comes to me I will never drive away.' The Son *acts* – 'for I have come down from heaven ... to do the will of him who sent me.' He is wholly dependent on the Father but he is *active*: being dependent has nothing to do with passivity or doing nothing.

In the Greek original these two verses are one sentence, linked by 'because' rather than 'for': it is *because* the Son has come down from heaven to do the Father's will that the Father gives to him, but the Father is paramount. Therefore the Father and the Son are rooted in each other in a constant circle of giving one to another, the foundation for the manner in which, in the later verse in John's gospel which I used for *Flying*, the identity of the sheep is rooted in that of the shepherd.

We have free will, which we tend to try and use to do 'what *I* want': that is, we try to be little gods, in charge of our own lives, because we think that this will give us freedom. The truth is closer to the reality that, because God designed human beings to be dependent on him, trying to be independent puts us in chains.

Unlike us Jesus Christ, who *is* God, is prepared to be a human being for our sake: dependent, surrendered, and free. (2)

What are the implications of this on how we live, and what does love in this context look like?

The story: In her present state Claire is completely dependent. Do you think that she is 'utterly worthless'? What might her 'value' be?

(2) This exciting idea is explored in Jane Williams' *Perfect Freedom* (see Bibliography).

Consider the journey that she, Jim and Matt have taken. What do you think that each of them has lost? What has each gained? Was it worth it?

Claire says that if things had been different, they might not have loved each other so much. Do you think she's right? If so, why?

10. Living (Be free)

My point of departure for this story was the following Bible passage:

One of the teachers of the law ... asked him, 'Of all the commandments, which is the most important?' 'The most important one', answered Jesus, 'is this: Hear, O Israel, the Lord our God, the Lord is one. Love the Lord your God with all your heart and with all your soul and with all your mind and with all your strength. The second is this: love your neighbour as yourself.'

Mark 12:28-31

The Bible verse: The teacher of the law asks Jesus this question during Holy Week, while Jesus is walking in the Temple courts in Jerusalem – after the triumphal entry and before the passion – so the timing is important. So is the setting, being the Jews' sacred Temple; and the courtyard where this discussion takes place is where the sacrifices were offered as required by Jewish law, including the lambs at Pentecost.

Jesus's reply begins with the 'Shema', the Jewish confession of faith (Deuteronomy 6:4) which pious Jews recited morning and evening and which to this day begins every synagogue service. He adds to it the natural development of loving one's neighbour as oneself (Leviticus 19:18).

Although it comes directly from Jewish scripture, this reply can be spoken by any non-Jew and transcends, as the teacher of the law immediately grasped, the whole system of sacrifices required of pious Jews.

Therefore Jesus, who is about to offer himself as the ultimate, once-for-all sacrifice for our sins, is both the fulfilment of the Jewish scripture and 'the mediator of a new covenant' that restores our access to God (as described for example in Hebrews 9:11-15). In him both come together – he is 'our peace', as Paul says in a different context (Ephesians 2:14-18).

And what Jesus suggests in his reply is that, because of his work here on earth, we are now *enabled* to fulfil these two commandments – as was not possible for the Jews before he came.

The story: What is Margaret like? What qualities of character and attitude in her earlier life do you think contributed to the person she is now?

Why do you think Margaret wasn't afraid when her house was broken into?

Think about Dan and Larry and Sue. In what ways do you think their lives might change as a result of knowing Margaret?

On the whole a life surrendered to God and to others probably has rather an ordinary, everyday aspect. Do you think that is so, and if so, why might that be?

If I'm to love my neighbour as myself, how do I love myself?

Bibliography

These are some of the books I either read for the first time or returned to with pleasure while writing this book. They are only here because you might enjoy them too.

Richard A. Burridge, *Four Gospels, One Jesus?* (SPCK, London, 1997)

Joan Chittister OSB, *The Rule of Benedict* (Crossroad Publishing Company, New York, 2005)

David Foster OSB, *Reading with God* (Continuum, London, 2005)

Gerard W Hughes, *God In All Things* (Hodder and Stoughton, London, 2004)

Christopher Jamison, *Finding Sanctuary* (Orion Publishing London, 2006)
Finding Happiness (Orion Publishing, 2008)

Julian of Norwich, *Revelations of Divine Love* (Penguin Books, Middlesex,1966)

Brother Lawrence, *The Practice of the Presence of God* (H R Allenson, London, 1906)

C S Lewis, *Mere Christianity* (HarperCollins, London, 2001)
The Great Divorce (HarperCollins, 2002)
The Abolition of Man (HarperCollins, 2001)

Sara Maitland, *A Big Enough God* (Mowbray, London, 1995)

Thomas Merton, *Contemplative Prayer* (Darton, Longman and Todd, London, 2005)

Alison Morgan, *The Wild Gospel* (Monarch Books, Oxford, 2004)

Henri Nouwen, *The Return of the Prodigal Son* (Darton, Longman and Todd, 1994)
The Way of the Heart (Darton, Longman and Todd, London, 1999)

Elizabeth Ruth Obbard, *Through Julian's Windows* (Canterbury Press, Norwich, 2008)

John Ortberg, *The Life You've Always Wanted* (Zondervan, Michigan, USA, 1997)
If You Want To Walk On Water, You've Got To Get Out Of The Boat (Zondervan, Michigan, USA, 2001)

Timothy Radcliffe OP, *I Call You Friends* (Continuum, London, 2001)
What is the Point of Being a Christian? (Continuum, London, 2005)

Eckhart Tolle, *The Power of Now* (Hodder and Stoughton, London, 1997)

Jean Vanier, *Becoming Human* (Darton, Longman and Todd, London, 1999)

Jane Williams, *Perfect Freedom* (Canterbury Press, Norwich, 2001)

Rowan Williams, *Silence and Honey Cakes* (Lion Hudson, Oxford, 2003)

Tom Wright, *John for Everyone, Parts I and II* (SPCK, London, 2002)
Mark for Everyone (SPCK, London, 2001)

Philip Yancey, *Reaching for the Invisible God* (Zondervan, Michigan, USA, 2000)

The Holy Bible:
New International Version Study Bible, Hodder and Stoughton, London, 2000

The New Greek-English Interlinear New Testament, ed J D Douglas, tr Robert K Brown and Philip N Comfort (Tyndale House Publishers Inc, Illinois USA, 1990)

Appendix: Burrswood Hospital

Half the proceeds of this book are going to support the work of Burrswood in Groombridge, just outside Tunbridge Wells, Kent.

Burrswood is a Christian Hospital and place of healing set in two hundred acres of beautiful Kentish countryside. It is a 40-bed, non-emergency hospital specialising in convalescence, rehabilitation, respite care and post-operative recovery. Its ethos of whole-person care ensures that people are looked after in body, mind and spirit through the team approach of resident physicians, nurses, counsellors, chaplains and physiotherapists.

Burrswood staff have become expert in long-term conditions such as multiple sclerosis and chronic fatigue syndrome/ME, and in palliative and end of life care. The busy Outpatient department provides physiotherapy, hydrotherapy and counselling.

Burrswood is a place of transformation, where people's lives are changed; and it isn't only the physically sick who find that this is so. Burrswood welcomes hundreds of day visitors a month to enjoy Bocky's tea room, the bookshop, extensive landscaped grounds and the beautiful Italianate church of Christ the Healer, where healing services are held on Thursday mornings and Saturday afternoons. It is a transforming and healing place to go for a restful day out, and for those who wish to stay longer, there is an attractive and comfortable guest house.

Many who see the profound difference that it regularly makes to those who come are often astonished to discover that Burrswood receives no government funding, and is dependent on its fees, donations and the income from its commercial activities.

Half the proceeds of the sale of this book will go to the Access to Care fund, which provides help for those who are not able to pay for the cost of their care. Thank you so much!

You can find out more about Burrswood on their website, www.burrswood.org.uk or by calling them on 01892 863637.